To Jay and
Kim interesting recount
of health status in PR
as seen through the
eyes of an Irish
Doctor.
The editorial notes
are also very stimulating
With love
Julia Anne Carter

A Sojourn in Tropical Medicine
Francis W. O´Connor´s Diary
of a Porto Rican Trip, 1927

A SOJOURN IN TROPICAL MEDICINE:

Francis W. O'Connor's Diary
of a Porto Rican Trip, 1927

elayed half an hour.   Only about 10 Anglo-Saxon

ssengers are Latin-American and are mostly

the Virgin Islands.

        Meals in two series.   I go to the

th nice Americans, one called Twee

Francis W. O' Connor
(Courtesy of the Rockefeller Archive Center)

Edited by

Raúl Mayo Santana

Annette B. Ramírez de Arellano

José G. Rigau-Pérez

A SOJOURN IN TROPICAL MEDICINE:

Francis W. O'Connor's Diary of a Porto Rican Trip, 1927

La Editorial

Universidad de Puerto Rico

A Sojourn in Tropical Medicine: Francis W. O'Connor's Diary of a Porto Rican Trip, 1927
Mayo-Santana, Raúl, et al. Editors

ISBN: 978-0-8477-1400-1

This publication was sponsored by the Institute of the History of the Health
Sciences (IHICIS) Office of the Dean for Academic Affairs Medical Sciences
Campus, University of Puerto Rico:
Editor in Chief: Raúl Mayo-Santana.
Associate Editors: Annette B. Ramírez de Arellano and José G. Rigau-Pérez.
Collaborating Editors: Ada Haiman Arena, Ángel A. Román-Franco and María
Concepción Hernández.

Designed by Félix L. Agosto jr

The authorization for publication by La Editorial, Universidad de Puerto Rico
(University of Puerto Rico Press) of *Francis William O'Connor's Diary of a Porto
Rican Trip*, October 27- November 21, 1927, was granted by The New York
Academy of Medicine.

Photo on page X courtesy of Archives and Special Collections, A.C. Long Health
Science Library, Columbia University.

Photo authorizations by: The New York Academy of Medicine, New York;
Special Collections, Hammer Health Sciences Center, Columbia University, New
York; Rockefeller Archive Center, Sleepy Hollow, New York.

Printed by Quebecor World Bogotá S.A.
Printed in Colombia

La Editorial
Universidad de Puerto Rico
P.O. Box23322, UPR Station
San Juan, Puerto Rico 00931-3322
www.laeditorialupr.com

CONTENTS

*This book is dedicated to those like O'Connor
who have contributed to the advancement
of the health sciences
in Puerto Rico and the Caribbean*

Many people have helped at various points in the preparation of this book; as Editors we thank them all.

Our first acknowledgment must go to Angeli Santana, graduate student at the School of Public Health, and Carmen Santos, Director of the Colección Puertorriqueña, Biblioteca Conrado F. Asenjo, Medical Sciences Campus, University of Puerto Rico, for their research assistance in procuring the materials and data used in the annotations to the diary. The reconstruction of the state of health in Puerto Rico in the 1920s and 1930s was made possible by the invaluable assistance provided by Lucy Peña Carro and Carmen Santos in accessing the rich archival and printed material in the Colección Puertorriqueña. We are also indebted to Wilma Cartagena, secretary at the School of Public Health, for her disinterested support of this and other IHICIS (Institute of the History of the Health Science) projects.

Special thanks go to Arlene Shaner, Reference Librarian of the Historical Collections at the New York Academy of Medicine, for helping us obtain permission from the Academy for the publication of O'Connor's diary; to Stephen E. Novak, Head of the Archives & Special Collections at the Augustus C. Long Health Sciences Library, Columbia University Medical Center, who, in recognition of the former relationship between Columbia University and the School of Tropical Medicine of the University of Puerto Rico, waived the fee for the four photographs of the School appearing in the book; and to Lee

Hiltzik of the Rockefeller Archive Center in Sleepy Hollow, New York for his invaluable help in documenting O'Connor's work at the Rockefeller Foundation. Arlene Shaner facilitated the use of O'Connor's papers, helped fill in gaps in the available documents, and arranged for the reproduction of photographs. Stephen Novak alerted us concerning primary sources, provided numerous leads, and tracked down information on Francis W. O'Connor. Lee Hiltzik was particularly helpful in answering queries, making documents available, and facilitating the photographic portraits of O'Connor that allow us to see him as he wished to present himself.

Thanks also to Caryl Guest of the Royal Society of Tropical Medicine who efficiently answered our requests; Victoria Killick, Archivist of the London School of Hygiene and Tropical Medicine, who provided access to multiple sources, the most important being the correspondence between O'Connor and Ronald Ross during World War I; and to Matthew McMahon who offered background information on Ireland, and suggested sources that enriched our understanding of the historical and cultural context that shaped O'Connor's youth.

We are profoundly grateful to Marta Aponte Alsina of the University of Puerto Rico Press for her strong advocacy and assistance during much of the project and to George V. Hillyer, Professor at the UPR School of Medicine for encouraging the publication of the book. We would also like to thank Gloria Madrazo Vicéns and Antonio C. Ramírez Morales of the UPR Press for their professional and kind editorial assistance.

Our deepest appreciation to UPR Medical Sciences Campus Chancellor José R. Carlo and Dean for Academic Affairs Delia M. Camacho for their warm and sustained support of IHICIS. We are grateful to the following friends, who read some of the essays closely and made many useful suggestions: José Becerra, Jacqueline Biscombe, Manuel Mayo López, Francisco Moscoso, Mark Oberle, Aida L. Quintero Noriega, Max Ramírez de Arellano (father and son), Jorge Rigau, Robert V. Tauxe, José M. Torres Gómez, Rosa Velasco, Gary Weil, and Sonia Yumet.

We reserve acknowledgment of our greatest debt for last—to the friends and colleagues, Silvia, Edgardo, Ada, Ángel and Concha, who contributed as essayists or collaborating editors of this edition of O'Connor's diary and whose intellectual excitement, rigor and generosity made this book possible and worthy.

The Editors

layed half an hour.   Only about 10 anglo-

ssengers are Latin-American and are mos

the Virgin Islands.

Meals in two series.   I go to

th nice Americans, one called Tweedy,

PREFACE

T he diary of Francis William O'Connor offers a fascinating snapshot of Puerto Rico during the brief but very intense eighteen-day visit in 1927 by this specialist in tropical medicine and officer of the Division of Medical Education of the Rockefeller Foundation. As stated in one of the accompanying essays, the diary "was neither a technical report nor intended for public view. Its candid and vivid language reflects the skills of a passionate and rigorous scientist, the discreet obsessions of a technician, the shades and shadows of an impressionistic painter, and the idiosyncratic shifts and insightful commentaries of a world traveler." Needless to say, the preconceptions and prejudices of the times are also indirectly highlighted by the diarist. Finding himself amidst the elite of Puerto Rico, it is from this vantage point that he describes the lives of the "poor" and their "tropical" illnesses. This unique and exceptional book sheds new light upon the history and development of public health and medicine in Puerto Rico, an aspect of history not well served to date.

To complement the diary and offer a more complete record of the period, this book includes an introduction and four essays written especially for this volume by prominent observers of the island's culture and history. A brief but comprehensive biographical essay on this "Irishman who loved the tropics" takes the reader from O'Connor's dark days in boarding school through to the heyday of his association with that pillar of tropical medicine, Sir Patrick Manson. The biography recounts O'Connor's experiences at the London School of Tropical Medicine, his work in the South East Asian tropics, his appointment as a Rockefeller officer and the culmination of his career with his appointment as professor of medicine at Columbia University. A second essay on the epidemiology, diseases and public health measures employed in 1927 adds the depth and background needed to better understand the nuances of O'Connor's diary. The third essay is an illuminating discussion of the genre of travel writing which is "characterized by the sharing of the 'I' and 'eye' of travelers as they visit new places." The final essay takes a more impressionistic approach to the subject, providing a contrasting literary and sociological perspective. When taken together, these essays and the diary felicitously combine to provide unique descriptions and assessments of the health challenges faced by Puerto Rico in 1927.

The diary also provides a lively portrait of life at the School of Tropical Medicine, its facilities, staff, activities and impact on the local medical culture. The School was the precursor of the present University of Puerto Rico School of Medicine; thus the diary provides a glimpse into the academic and operational traditions that became the foundation of the latter institution. The footnotes constitute an exceptionally informative addition to the work; they specify and expand upon authors, books, conditions, diseases, physicians, the Puerto Rico leper colony, landmark buildings, regions, the tuberculosis sanatorium, etc. In summary, they are a rich and powerful complement to the diary. The footnotes alone make this book worthwhile for the person interested in the period.

It should be highlighted that Dr. O'Connor's diary spans critical political and economic moments on the island, yet nowhere does he allow those dire days to percolate through its content. On the contrary, his portrayal of Puerto Rico, its people, its environment and accomplishments at the time foreshadows his upbeat conclusion that "One feels that before long Porto Rico should make valuable contributions to medicine." This book takes the tight and focused narrative presented by O'Connor and employs it to launch a richly detailed and coherent view of the author and his subject.

George V. Hillyer, Ph.D
Professor,
Department of Pathology and Laboratory Medicine
School of Medicine, Medical Sciences Campus
University of Puerto Rico.
Secretary-Treasurer,
The American Society of Tropical Medicine and Hygiene.

School of Tropical Medicine
(Courtesy of Archives and Special Collections,
A.C. Long Health Science Library, Columbia University)

INTRODUCTION

Raúl Mayo-Santana

In 1927, Francis William O'Connor, a specialist in tropical medicine and an officer at the Division of Medical Education of the Rockefeller Foundation, arrived in Puerto Rico to lecture at the relatively new School of Tropical Medicine. During his 18 days in Puerto Rico, O'Connor gave three scientific and two general lectures, visited health officers and institutions across the island, held clinical consultations with patients, collected and dissected mosquitoes as part of his field research on filariasis, participated in a variety of social events, took photographs, painted scenic landscapes, and kept a diary of the entire trip.

The diary was neither a technical report nor intended for public view. Its candid and vivid language reflects the skills of a passionate and rigorous scientist, the discreet obsessions of a technician, the shades and shadows of an impressionistic painter, and the idiosyncratic shifts and insightful commentaries of a world traveler. O'Connor's observations reveal the pretensions and hidden prejudices of a 'universal' scientist and the assumptions of an expert in a medical specialty born in the colonial tropics and established in the imperialist metropolis. At the same time, the author shows us the compassion and empathy of a masterful clinician and the fraternal camaraderie of a sympathetic colleague. The visit of Francis W. O'Connor coincides with a moment in which the sociopolitical situation in Puerto Rico was turning from tension and conflict into turmoil; this context, however, is not manifested in the diarist's flights of optimism and his perception of a "craze for learning" among the islanders. Puerto Rico became a colony of the United States in 1898, and was under a military regime until 1900, when the U.S. Congress enacted a 'transitory' law that remained in force up to 1917. Through the rapid annexation of the island, the United States achieved its expansionist goal of establishing a secure military stronghold and naval base in the Caribbean. During the first years of U.S. rule, the economy of Puerto Rico became increasingly structurally integrated into the economy of the United States, a transformation that promoted the economic and political interests of the latter—in fact, "government measures like the extension of tariff protection to Puerto Rico made the production of such commodities as sugar and tobacco highly profitable."[1]

The Foraker Act of 1900 placed the people of Puerto Rico under a government run primarily by U.S. civilians appointed by the War Department and the president, with the advice or consent of Congress. Puerto Ricans participated as a minority in an Executive Council, which served as the governor's cabinet and had both executive and legislative powers. The law created an elective legislature (*Cámara de Delegados*), but the governor had veto power over its decisions. The act also created the elective position of resident commissioner in Washington, with a 'voice' but no vote on behalf of Puerto Rican interests before federal agencies. In its constitutional aspects, the organic act eventually broke judicial ground for a new kind of non-incorporated

---

1   Perloff, H.S. *Puerto Rico's Economic Future: A Study in Planned Development.* Chicago: The University of Chicago Press, 1950: 27.

territory, in which the colonial condition was boldly reaffirmed;[2] locally, however, the occasion for direct resistance would come with some delay.[3] During the first two decades of the twentieth century, the land and its people became the subject of what has been called the "*cañaveralización* of Puerto Rico"[4] or the "ascent of sugar."[5] With the near collapse of the coffee industry produced by the upheavals that accompanied the change of sovereignty, sugar and tobacco interests predominated over all others. However, the expansion of sugarcane and tobacco crops and the beginning of manufacturing led to the growth and organization of the labor movement. Thus, the period between 1915 and 1919 was a propitious climate,[6] both in its economic as well as in its political expressions, for labor unrest and uprisings. Equally important, since the early days of the military occupation, the U.S. government followed a clear policy of annexation of the country and "Americanization" of the population,[7] which provoked nationalist sentiments and nurtured cultural and political resistance.

In 1917, during World War I, the political colonial

---

2   Trías Monge, José. *Puerto Rico. The Trials of the Oldest Colony in the World.* New Haven and London: Yale University Press, 1977: "The doctrine of the selective, nonautomatic applicability of the Constitution and the consequent plenary powers of Congress to govern the new possessions...": 41.

3   Scarano, Francisco. *Puerto Rico. Cinco Siglos de Historia.* 2nd. ed. México: McGraw-Hill, 2000; 718.

4   Picó, Fernando. *Historia general de Puerto Rico.* Río Piedras: Editorial Huracán, 1988: Ch. 13.

5   Dietz, James L. *Economic History of Puerto Rico. Institutional Change and Capitalist Development.* Princeton, NJ: Princeton University Press, 1986: 103-106.

6   Picó, F. *Historia general*, op. cit.: 241.

7   Negrón de Montilla, A. *Americanization in Puerto Rico and the Public School System, 1900-1930.* Río Piedras: Editorial Edil, 1971.

system changed somewhat as a reaction to nationalistic urges and unrest. Congress enacted a new law, the Jones Act, which conceded and imposed U.S. citizenship[8] on the inhabitants of Puerto Rico.[9] The statute created a new elective bicameral legislature, limited, as in the United States, to male voters 21 years of age or older. Despite these advances toward greater civic representation, the governorship remained a presidential appointment and the governor's cabinet still required approval by the U.S. Senate. The Jones Act represented a significant political advance over the previous law,[10] but some of its clauses reinforced the economic dependency of the country.[11] One economist has summarized the era as one in which "Puerto Rico suffered the consequences of land monopoly, absentee ownership, and monoculture, with the inevitable creation of a large class of seasonally employed field workers…"[12] While the social and living conditions of the population improved in some aspects during the first decades after the U.S. occupation,

---

8   The characterization of the act that granted U.S. citizenship as both a concession and an imposition raises the issue of the paradoxical nature of the event. From the side of the imperialist forces and their local allies, it was the bestowal of Americanization. From the point of view of the political elites, who resisted U.S. citizenship, it represented a coercive act and a loss of autonomy. The tension between the resistance and acceptance of this dubious gift has been a major factor in a colonial history marked by both collaboration and non-collaboration.

9   According to José Trías Monge, *The Trials*, op. cit., "American citizenship was conferred in a most inelegant way. Official Washington did not care about the appearance of coercion that permeated the whole process… ": 76.

10   Ibid.: "The Jones Act reaffirmed instead the decision to keep Puerto Rico as an increasingly Americanized colony, on the road to self-government, but always to be securely subject to the sovereignty of the United States.": 76.

11   Picó, F. *Historia general*, op. cit.: 244-245.

12   Perloff, H.S. *Puerto Rico's Economic Future*, op. cit.: 29.

by the 1920s the social and economic conditions, in general, were deteriorating and becoming critical.[13]

During the first years of U.S. control, public health policy in Puerto Rico was characterized by an absence of cultural adaptation in the imposition of sanitary measures, and tension between local needs and outside expertise. At the same time, local expectations were frustrated by the gap between promised resources and actual performance.[14] Health care "showed some significant improvements under U.S. control, in part as the result of such measures as smallpox vaccination," but, "in other respects, much remained to be done."[15] One final assessment was that during the first three decades of U.S. rule, "there were gains in health care, but the health problems associated everywhere with poverty and human degradation continued."[16]

O'Connor came to Puerto Rico to teach and carry out research at the School of Tropical Medicine, one year and a

---

13   Ibid.: 30.

14   See, among others: Silvestrini, Blanca G. "El impacto de la política de salud pública de los Estados Unidos en Puerto Rico, 1898-1913." In Blanca G. Silvestrini, ed. *Politics, society and culture in the Caribbean. Selected papers of the XIV Conference of Caribbean Historians.* San Juan: Universidad de Puerto Rico and Association of Caribbean Historians, 1893: 67-83; Rigau-Pérez, J.G. "Strategies that led to the eradication of smallpox in Puerto Rico, 1882-1921." *Bulletin of the History of Medicine 1985*; 59: 75-88; and Ramírez de Arellano, Annette B. "La planificación de los servicios de salud en Puerto Rico." *Revista Interamericana de Planificación* 1978; 12: 118-126.

15   Dietz, J.L. Economic History, op. cit.: 128-129.

16   Ibid.: 133. Francisco Scarano, *Puerto Rico*, op. cit., has also mentioned that, "Si bien algunas campañas de salud pública, como la de la anemia, se apuntaron triunfos—completos o parciales—, otras no lograron contrarrestar la influencia de las condiciones de vida sufridas por el pueblo trabajador. Por ejemplo, la tuberculosis causó cada vez mayores estragos.": 692. Regarding the tuberculosis problem, see for example: Garrido Morales, Eduardo. "Program for Tuberculosis Control in Puerto Rico." *Journal of the American Medical Association* 1935; 105: 1842-1844.

few months after its opening. The origins of the School date back to the 1904 government-sponsored Anemia Commission. The Commission, created to address the anemia associated with hookworm disease that was widely prevalent among the population, eventually evolved into the Institute of Tropical Medicine and Hygiene in the years 1912-1913. Both institutions were important precursors of the School of Tropical Medicine of the University of Puerto Rico. The Commission and the Institute emerged from the scientific and humanitarian work and collaboration among resident physicians from the United States and Puerto Rico. Founders such as Bailey K. Ashford, Pedro Gutiérrez-Igaravidez, Walter King and Isaac González-Martínez were among the leading medical scientists on the island, and had acquired a degree of international prestige and recognition in the field of tropical medicine. They clearly understood that the work of the Institute needed a broad and stable foundation in order to consolidate its research and educational activities. Thus, the creation of a graduate school of tropical medicine, under the auspices of a major school of medicine from the United States, became a priority for them. In 1926, following negotiations between the Government of Puerto Rico and Columbia University, the School of Tropical Medicine was created.[17] The School was primarily oriented towards research on tropical diseases and the post-graduate education of physicians interested in research and treatment of illnesses most often found in warm climates. It became a leading institution in field and laboratory research in tropical medicine and attracted scientists and students from all over the

---

17   Ramírez de Arellano, Annette B. "Columbia's Overseas Venture: The School of Tropical Medicine at the University of Puerto Rico." *Medicine's Geographic Heritage* 1989; 5: 35-40.

world. As Annette Ramírez de Arellano mentions in her essay, "the imposing citadel housing the School of Tropical Medicine was the most obvious symbol of the importance accorded the public's health," but "not the only major achievement," at the time of O'Connor's visit and travelogue.

This was the time and context, the moment and place, the 'deplorable,' but 'congenial tropical environment,' which served as a backdrop to the gaze and impressions of O'Connor's *Diary of a Porto Rican Trip*,[18] of 1927. Even when the diarist's views on Puerto Rico's health and social conditions were based on generally sound background and contemporary information, he and his hosts seem to be totally unaware of the early (1899) debate concerning the usurpation of the name of the country, "*Porto* Rico."[19]

While most definitely a "period piece," O'Connor's chronicle was deemed rich and valuable enough by the essayists and editors of this book to warrant its publication and our commentaries. The decision to publish in English is based on the editors' desire to secure the diarist's own voice. Furthermore, this publication is aimed at readers who not only read English but also appreciate having access to the original document. O'Connor's diary has been selected as the first publication of the Institute of the History of the Health Sciences (IHICIS) because of its historical and scientific significance.

---

18   O'Connor named his diary, *Diary of Porto Rican Trip*; the insertion of the indefinite article "a" is only an editorial device.

19   García, Gervasio L. "I am the other: Puerto Rico in the eyes of North Americans, 1898." *Journal of American History* June 2000; 87 (1): 39-64. According to García: "naming was a form of domination; the imperial appetite was not sated until it had appropriated every bit of the island, even its name": 51.

The origin of this project dates back to April 2004 when IHICIS advisor José Rigau came across a copy of O'Connor's typewritten manuscript that had been provided to the Conrado F. Asenjo Library at the Medical Sciences Campus of the University of Puerto Rico by José Curet, Professor of History at The University of the Sacred Heart. Rigau got in touch with another IHICIS advisor, Annette Ramírez de Arellano, who had encountered the manuscript over 20 years earlier, when doing research for her dissertation. Rigau suggested it merited reprinting. Five months later Rigau and Ramírez de Arellano met Silvia Rabionet and me, both IHICIS directors, at a conference and took the opportunity to share their thoughts on the O'Connor diary and recommend its printing. Over the following weeks this project came to life as the four of us discussed the personal, social, historical, scientific and literary context required to fully appreciate the significance of the diary. Much later, I approached Edgardo Rodríguez Juliá to contribute a literary critique. The working group continued to grow as Concha Hernández, Ángel Román Franco and Ada Haiman joined us as collaborators in the editing of the text. We had the good fortune of finding in Marta Aponte Alsina, then at the University of Puerto Rico Press, a facilitator and advocate for the book. Finally, George Hillyer, an international expert in tropical medicine, accepted our invitation to write a preface to this work, thus bringing the endeavor to a felicitous close.

O'Connor is a unique foreigner: an invited scientist and scholar, a doctor in medicine and parasitology with expertise and experience in tropical medicine around the world, and a program officer of the Rockefeller Foundation. He came to lecture, do research, and offer clinical consultations at the

University of Puerto Rico's School of Tropical Medicine under the auspices of Columbia University (where O'Connor went to work after his visit to Puerto Rico). As other authors mention in their essays in this book, "O'Connor was witness to a singular moment in the history of public health and medical institutions in Puerto Rico" (José Rigau) and "O'Connor's chronicle reflects an outsider's view of the island at the time of great effervescence in the health field" (Annette Ramírez de Arellano). Silvia Rabionet adds that O'Connor's diary "invites us to reflect upon the observer and the observed, when two cultures come into close encounter through the discerning eyes of an avid scientist." Edgardo Rodríguez Juliá concludes that "O'Connor is the traveler who wants only a cultivated vision of the visited country; he eschews condescension, is lavish in praise, and sparing in his criticisms."

This book contains an edited and annotated version of O'Connor's *Diary of a Porto Rican Trip*. The original hand and typewritten manuscripts of the diary are on file in the archives of the New York Academy of Medicine. The book also contains four essays which seek to expand and clarify the diary's historical and scientific significance. The first of these is a biography of Francis William O'Connor, *An Irishman Who Loved the Tropics*, by Annette B. Ramírez de Arellano. Who was Francis W. O'Connor, and what prompted his trip to Puerto Rico? An Irishman by birth, trained in England, who eventually became a U.S. citizen, O'Connor was a physician and parasitologist who managed to feel at home wherever he happened to be. In her essay, Ramírez de Arellano has reconstructed his "examined life." Following the Victorian tradition, O'Connor kept journals and ended many a work day recording his experiences and opinions. At the same time, some of O'Connor's peers and students also recorded their impressions of the man. Thus, we are able to see O'Connor not only as he wished to present himself, but also as others saw him.

Dr. José G. Rigau-Pérez's essay, *The Apogee of Tropical Medicine: An Epidemiologic Portrait of Puerto Rico in 1927*, provides an epidemiologic description of the conditions which prevailed at the time of O'Connor's visit, and a historical account of the health facilities and social institutions mentioned in the diary, from before O'Connor's arrival to the time when the diseases and health programs disappeared. O'Connor's chronicle invites the reader to explore travel writing as a literary genre. In the third essay, *Travel Writing: Close Encounters through Discerning Eyes*, Silvia E. Rabionet summarizes the genre's evolving history from ancient to contemporary times. Travel writing has rapidly expanded as a field of study and travel narratives have increasingly become a source for examining issues of power, self-perception, and cultural representation. This documented overview of the genre provides information to the reader for a more in-depth and rich appreciation of O'Connor's diary.

The final essay, by novelist Edgardo Rodríguez Juliá, *Through a Traveler's Eyes: Landscape and Lore in Francis W. O'Connor's Diary of a Porto Rican Trip*, presents a literary appreciation of O'Connor's narrative. This view of the scientific diarist by a writer of fiction thus offers a lucid diagnosis, not only of the chronicler's use of language and creativity, but also of his biases and prejudices. The final essay therefore captures the essence of O'Connor's enthrallment with the tropics.

The publication of this narrative piece does not ignore the fact that O'Connor was an Irish scientist working in the "exotic" field of tropical medicine. He arrives in Puerto Rico from the colonial center, although he would characterize himself as a humanitarian and his role as that of "universal" doctor and scientist. These designations carry a questionable connotation of political neutrality. Therefore, this volume seeks to add a more nuanced interpretation of the O'Connor diary. Through the unique integration of both scientific and literary perspectives, it reveals the dialectic interaction between colonizer and colonized.

Francis W. O' Connor
(Courtesy of the Rockefeller Archive Center)

1

Francis W. O'Connor's

Diary of a Porto Rican Trip

Diary of Porto Rican Trip
October 27 – November 21, 1927

Thursday,
October 27, 1927.

U p betimes and after breakfast packed. Then by taxi over Brooklyn Bridge to Atlantic Basin Pier 35—a difficult place to get to and taking three-quarters of an hour. Jam and confusion on the pier, but eventually got on board. Nice ship. Good cabin 103 and have it to myself. D.'s[1] roses arrived and made the room look very cheery. Boat due to sail at 12 but delayed half an hour. Only about 10 Anglo-Saxons on board. The rest of the passengers are Latin-American and are mostly from Porto Rico, Santo Domingo or the Virgin Islands.[2]

Meals in two series. I go to the first. Two men at my table—both nice Americans, one called Tweedy.

Sea calm. Making myself at home. The rest is pleasant

---

1   Referent unidentified.

2   See map of the region at site: http://memory.loc.gov/cgi-bin/map_item.pl.

after the rush. Finished reading Deeping's "Kitty,"[3] a good book. Went to sleep early.

Friday,
October 28, 1927.

Getting rough. Long head swell, rain, wind, grey, misty. Met Britisher at second meal at my table—A. T. Kerr, *aet.* [*age*] 24. North of Ireland. Very nice chap. In linen business, representing American branch of Irish linen firm. Discusses linen. Best from N. of Ireland, then French. Also demand in U.S. for linen of Belgium and Germany. Import 90% duty. The French raise their charges according to every change in franc—raise by percentage. Embroidering handkerchiefs now very popular. Swiss embroidery best and most expensive, then Irish. Now trying Porto Rican. Good but Porto Ricans very unreliable at working and no matter what they are paid may stop work at any time. K.[err][4] thinks of going to China as the Chinese are now in the trade, especially the embroidery part of it. O'C[5] says the Chinese are second to no one and advises K. to make a trip to spy out the land. K. is a curious chap. Four years in U.S. Lives at Montclair in N.J. Has lots of acquaintances but <u>no</u>

---

3   *Kitty* (1927), a novel written by George Davidson (Warwick) Deeping (1877-1950), an English novelist and short story writer and a bestselling writer in both Europe and America in the 1920s and 1930s. *Kitty* is an inter-war bestseller about a young officer afraid of going to the front who finds hope in the shopgirl daughter of an impoverished doctor. Deeping, like his father and grandfather, trained as a doctor. Later, he gave up his medical practice to become a full-time writer. (See Mary Grover. "Deeping, Warwick." *The Literary Encyclopedia*, Online database. 8 November 2002.)

4   O'Connor makes use throughout the diary of the initials of a person's name who he has previously mentioned. In order to facilitate the reading, we will henceforth spell out the name of the person mentioned, except where the initial's referent is obvious.

5   O'Connor, himself.

<u>friends</u>. We have a few drinks and spend much of the time in talk.

Passed Cape Hatteras off North Carolina where we expected bad weather, but it now became calm and pleasant. It is now getting warm. I have not worn a top coat since starting.

Saturday,
October 29, 1927.

Perfectly calm. Crew change to white ducks. Sea tropical blue. Horizon tropically clear. Sky at night tropically clear with brilliant stars. It's good to be back or going back.

Dr. F. W. Hoogan, practitioner at St. Croix in Virgin Islands, tells O'C as follows: Virgin Islands: Two important cities—St. Croix, pop. 9,000, 60 miles from San Juan in Porto Rico—6 hours by naval boat or small passenger boat; St. Thomas, pop. 7,000. Natives of both Negro. Some Danish firms. American naval station. U.S. Navy doctors have done much to clean up disease. Those now prevalent: dengue[6] and filariasis;[7] previously malaria[8] prevalent but not now since oiling measures were adopted against mosquito larvae.

---

6   An infectious, eruptive, febrile, viral disease of tropical areas, transmitted by Aedes mosquitoes. (*Dorland's Pocket Medical Dictionary*, 23rd ed. Philadelphia: Saunders, 1982.)

7   Filariasis. Wuchereria bancrofti (the parasite present in Puerto Rico in O'Connor's day), Brugia malayi, or B. timori larvae, transmitted by mosquitoes, lodge in the lymph tissue and the lungs and may produce nocturnal asthma, chronic lung disease, renal disease, arthritis, and inflammation of lymph nodes and lymph vessels. There was no medication to treat filariasis in 1927.

8   An infectious febrile disease caused by any of four protozoan Plasmodium species (falciparum, malariae, ovale, and vivax), transmitted by Anopheles mosquitoes. It produces fever, chills, sweats, and headache for a week to a month or longer, with relapses at irregular intervals for years thereafter, unless the proper antibiotic is provided. In 1927, patients were treated with quinine capsules for at least two months.

In the evening A. T. Kerr, W.G. House (Chief Steward) and O'C sat at the stern in the dark enjoying the view of the stars. Presently the soft strumming of the guitar was heard. It was played by a Porto Rican sitting nearby and soon his companion began to sing some delightful Spanish songs. This impromptu concert will not be forgotten. The dark night, the quiet, the warmth of the Tropics, and then the soft, soothing rhythm of the melodies!

Sunday,
October 30, 1927.

Lazy. Breakfast in bed. First time for years—therefore the more enjoyable, this luxury. Head swell and ship pitching; but sky, horizon and atmosphere very clear. Flying fish small ones. Plenty of brown and yellow seaweed and the sea is a deep blue.

Monday,
October 31, 1927.

Last night was oppressively hot. Heavy rain fell and the ship's siren blew at intervals, so I had very little sleep. I dressed at 5 A.M. and went on deck to find the rain coming down with the tropical intensity which obscures all views. The ship had stopped just outside the Strait between the little reef-bound islet on the right that till last year housed the leper colony,[9] and on the left the challenging fortress of El Morro; through the mist I could see only the shadow of the latter, while the islet was not visible. Gradually dawn came and we steamed slowly along the tortuous channel between the buoys in the Strait, and passing close to the old Spanish wall of San Juan, the Fortaleza (now

---

9   The leper colony was located in the islet known as Isla de Cabras.

the Governor's palace) and the quarantine station,[10] the ship turned in a semi-circle to the left and soon came alongside the quay. There was no delay about getting ashore and Lambert[11] met me at the gangway. Collecting my baggage, we went to his car and were driven away by his man, Jenaro,[12] passing through old San Juan, the new capitol, built on the American plan, the Tropical School[13] of Spanish design, the Cathedral of Notre Dame,[14] and a shopping section, then turning to the left over a bridge past the Fort [San] Gerónimo,[15] we reached the isthmus on which the Condado Vanderbilt Hotel[16] stands. The hotel is a large wooden four story building, salmon pink in color, with red brick tile roofing. It is surrounded by palms, hibiscus, kannas, and other tropical flowers and bushes. The front faces

10   O'Connor must refer to the Quarantine Hospital, because the Quarantine Station was located at the end of the bay (Miraflores).

11   Robert A. Lambert, MD (1907, Tulane), a pathologist specialized in tropical medicine who was appointed, in 1925, by Columbia University as the first director of the School of Tropical Medicine. At the moment of his appointment, Lambert was in Saõ Paulo, Brazil, where he was sent, in 1921, by the Rockefeller Foundation to direct the Pathological Institute. See also: Carmichael, E.B. "Robert Archibald Lambert. Pathologist-Teacher-Physician." *J Med Assoc State Alabama*, 1963 Feb; 32 (8): 232-234.

12   Genaro Martell appears on a list of salaried appointments to the School of Tropical Medicine, for the year July 1927-June 1928, as Mechanic Since there was no man called "Jenaro" on this list, it is reasonable to infer that "Jenaro" was indeed "Genaro Martell." "Minutes of the Special Board of Trustees of the University of Puerto Rico for the School of Tropical Medicine held May 11, 1927." Archivo Central, UPR.

13   See: http://medweb.rcm.upr.edu/history.php.

14   See photo at site: http://www.travel-images.com/view.shtml?puerto-rico8.jpg. O'Connor refers to the Iglesia de San Agustín in Puerta de Tierra.

15   A small fort located at the entrance to what is known today as Condado Lagoon in San Juan, built during the 17th century. See: http://en.wikipedia.org/wiki/Fort_San_Jeronimo.

16   In 1919, Cornelius Vanderbilt built the Condado Vanderbilt Hotel in the Condado, using the architects who designed Grand Central Station in New York City.

La Laguna del Condado. View from my window at Condado Vanderbilt Hotel
(Photo and comment: F.W. O'Connor)
(Courtesy of the Malloch Rare Book Room of the New York Academy of Medicine Library)

the sea and commands a splendid view of rocks, sand and bays, while promontory after promontory can be seen on the right, getting smaller and smaller as they fade in the changing shades of green, blue and purple colors towards the horizon. The entrance side of the hotel (in which, on the second floor, is my room #214) faces a view no less attractive. From my window I see in the foreground a grove of closely planted coconut trees with interspersed bamboos and poinsettias, while nearer the grounds a profusion of crotons of varying shades create a pleasing mixture of bright colors. Immediately beyond is the calm blue shining water of the still Condado Lagoon[17] from

---

17   One of San Juan's most noted landmarks, between Puerta de Tierra, Miramar and El Condado.

which arises on the distant shore a sloping hill, the sides and top of which are crowded with pink, blue, yellow, and brown houses with here and there a group of coconut trees or a few royal palms raising their heads towards the sky; and in the further distance, when it is fine, the purple summits of the mountains in the interior complete the picture. Stretching to the right, one sees the bridge connecting the San Juan Isthmus with the mainland, and further away the myriad colors of the city itself gradually fading in the distance in grays, mauve and bluish tints. On the left, nestling amongst rich coconut groves and surrounded by gardens vivid with bright colored plants and flowers, are the pretty houses of the residential suburb of Santurce.

But there is little time to study these prospects now, for while I wash and change in the bathroom R.A.L.[18] discusses his plans and my program for the weeks to come, and it is clear that I am going to be busy. He has left nothing to chance and every moment is cared for and all the appointments have already been made.

We first visited the Tropical School on the main thoroughfare through San Juan between the Capitol[19] and the Cathedral of Notre Dame. The school building is a combination of the beautiful and the practical, and demonstrates the fact that with but little extra expense the most useful buildings may be made pleasing to the eye. The three-story building with brick tiled roof and with verandahs

---

18   O'Connor frequently uses the initials "RAL" to refer to Lambert.

19   The Capitol was built between 1925 and 1929; however, the dome was not completed until 1961.

School of Tropical Medicine
(Courtesy of Archives and Special Collections,
A.C. Long Health Science Library, Columbia University)

bordered by Spanish arches, is surrounded by hibiscus trees and is fronted by large plots of the most vivid green grass on each side of the entrance path. Inside there is enough space for all and some room for working visitors, but one notices with pleasure the absence of superfluous accommodations. Here one is conscious of the fact that every inch of space not only will be used but is being used. The ground or entrance floor is for administration and stores. The first floor is occupied by the laboratories, class and technicians' rooms of the Parasitology Department on the east side, while on the west side of the same floor are similar accommodations for the Chemistry Department. The staff lunches in an ample section of the classroom for chemistry. The Library of the school occupies a large portion of the center of this floor. The top or third floor has quarters on a similar plan to the foregoing for bacteriology and pathology, while in the center of this floor is a large auditorium for lectures. On the two upper floors there are some comfortable rooms to be used as offices or laboratories for visiting workers, while on the second floor in addition there is an office for the Commissioner of Health, who is Professor of Hygiene and Communicable Diseases.[20] The whole building is constructed with a view to providing maximum lighting and free circulation of air, and the general impression of the visitor is of complete comfort without luxury. Behind the school and facing the sea a hospital is being constructed

---

20   O'Connor refers to Dr. Pedro N. Ortiz.

which will accommodate 45 bed patients. On this occasion I lunched with the following members of the staff:

Dr. R. A. Lambert,   Director

Dr. W. A. Hoffman,[21] Parasitology

Dr. D. H. Cook,[22]   Chemistry

Miss Trina Rivera,[23] Cook's Assistant

R.A.L. placed at my disposal a comfortable laboratory in the East portion of the building on the second floor. After I had arranged my lantern slides, etc., R.A.L. and I drove to the Municipal Hospital, where he did an autopsy on a suicide (the third of this kind that he has done in Puerto Rico). Suicides are fairly common and are generally connected to love affairs. The commonest method (as in this case) is by taking corrosive sublimate tablets; ten had been taken in this instance. The stomach contained a large ulcer, where the tablets had apparently rested, and there was extensive thrombosis in

---

21   William Albert Hoffman, D.Sc. (1924, Johns Hopkins), Professor of Parasitology at the School of Tropical Medicine since 1926. He conducted research with mosquitoes as transmitters of filariasis, which was one of O'Connor's main interests and published articles on schistosomiasis, Fasciola hepatica, and filariasis.

22   Donald H. Cook, Ph.D (1923, Columbia), Professor of Chemistry at the School of Tropical Medicine, from 1925 to 1944. He published several research articles related to food chemistry and nutrition. Once, member of the Junta Insular de Sanidad de Puerto Rico. (Conrado Asenjo ed. *Quién es Quién en Puerto Rico*, 1941-42. 3rd Ed. San Juan: Real Hermanos: 66.)

23   Trina Rivera, BA (1927, Columbia) appeared on a list of salaried appointments to the School of Tropical Medicine, for the year July 1927-June 1928, as Assistant in Chemistry. "Minutes of the Special Board of Trustees of the University of Puerto Rico for the School of Tropical Medicine held May 11, 1927." Archivo Central, UPR. She published research articles on food chemistry and nutrition.

and around the ulcerated area. There were hemorrhages and some ulceration of the small intestine and in addition some evidence of aspiration pneumonia. Whipworms,[24] ascaris[25] and ankylostomes[26] were found in the intestines and some of them were alive, a point worth noting in connection with the considerable amount of the poison that must have passed through the intestines.

Some points imparted by R.A.L. today:

He has done 80 postmortems in a year and a few months. There is very little rheumatism and practically no valvular disease in Porto Rico and until lately very few cases of lobar pneumonia due to pneumococci. Syphilitic aortic is rare. The commonest causes of death in children are marasmus[27] and the infantile diarrheas.

We visited Dr. Pedro Ortiz,[28] Government Commissioner

---

24   Trichuris trichiura, is the species principally infecting man of intestinal nematode (roundworms) parasites. Trichuriasis, an infection with Trichuris. (*Dorland's Pocket*; op.cit.: 694.)

25   A genus of large intestinal nematode parasites. Ascariasis, infection with this roundworm which is parasitic in the human intestine. After ingestion, the larvae migrate first to the lungs then to the intestine. (*Dorland's Pocket*; op.cit.: 76.)

26   A genus of hookworms, including Necator americanus (American or New World hookworm), parasitic in the small intestine and a cause of hookworm disease. (*Dorland's Pocket*; op.cit.: 36.)

27   Severe malnutrition affecting infants and children, especially of impoverished regions, that is characterized by poor growth, loss of subcutaneous fat, muscle atrophy, apathy, and pronounced weight loss. (*Medline Plus Medical Dictionary*)

28   Pedro N. Ortiz, MD (1919, Boston), Puerto Rico Commissioner of Health, 1923-1930. Professor of Hygiene and Transmissible Diseases at the School of Tropical Medicine, 1926-30. (*Quién es Quién en Puerto Rico*, 1933-34; op. cit.: 115.)

of Health, whom I had met previously in Dr. Darrach's[29] office at College of Physicians and Surgeons, New York. He was very friendly and courteous and made arrangements for me to study many activities under his administration.

In the evening I attended a delightful dinner given by R.A.L. at the Union Club,[30] at which there were about 25 persons present, including the following, with whom I am to become well acquainted: Drs. Garry N. Burke,[31] Ortiz, Fernós Isern,[32] Serra,[33]

29   William Darrach, MD, Dean of the College of Physicians and Surgeons, New York, Columbia University, 1919-30. He participated, as an officer of Columbia University, in the creation of the School of Tropical Medicine and was a renowned leader in medical education.

30   A social club established in 1908 by and for North Americans. It was located on Olimpo Street in Miramar, where the Puerto Rico Department of Justice has its current headquarters. The club had a splendid reading room, meeting room, pool, and restaurants. From this site, its members enjoyed a privileged view of the San Antonio bay, which connects the Condado Lagoon with the San Juan Bay.

31   Garry N. Burke, MD (1918, Buffalo), Instructor in Tropical Medicine and Surgery at the School of Tropical Medicine. "Faculty list, 1927-28." Archivo Central, UPR.

32   Antonio Fernós Isern, MD (1915, Maryland), cardiologist, Puerto Rico Commissioner of Health (1931-1933 and 1942-46) and Professor of Hygiene at the School of Tropical Medicine, since 1933. During O'Connor's visit, he was Assistant Commissioner of Health (1920-31). (Quién es Quién en Puerto Rico, 1933-34, op.cit.: 67-68.)

33   Américo Serra Colón, MD (1923, Rush, Chicago), doctor in medicine with a certificate in tropical medicine. He was one of the first sixteen students registered in the School of Tropical Medicine for its first term (October 1926-January 1927). Serra appears on a list of salaried appointments to the School of Tropical Medicine, for July 1927-June 1928, as Instructor in Tropical Medicine. "Minutes of the Special Board of Trustees of the University of Puerto Rico for the School of Tropical Medicine held May 11, 1927." Archivo Central, UPR. Also, during O'Connor's visit, he was a resident at the Presbyterian Hospital, 1924-28.

Goyco (from Ponce),[34] Carrión,[35] Ramón Suárez,[36] etc.

It was inspiring to note the genuinely good spirit in which the Spanish and American doctors mix and cooperate, especially in view of the clearly bad feeling which exists outside the profession between Porto Ricans and what they designate their U. S. "masters." It was especially noticeable with what great respect and confidence the Porto Rican medicos look upon R.A.L. as both man and leader. This experience confirms my reflections on the potentiality of scientists, and especially of medical ones, to smash nationalism and eventually bring about good will amongst the various nationalities. In all countries scientists are doing more than anyone else to spread good feeling, but they are seriously handicapped by political agents and by uneducated and ill-bred tourists.

The conversation at dinner was politely turned to matter other than medical and my hosts told me many stories of the terrible barracuda and the shark in local waters. The following personal experiences are worth noting:

---

34   In 1948-49, a Dr. José A. Goyco is listed as Associate in Chemistry in the Department of Chemistry and Nutrition at the School of Tropical Medicine.

35   Arturo L. Carrión Pacheco, MD (1919, Havana), was one of the twenty students registered in the School of Tropical Medicine for its second term (February-May 1927). He was a dermatologist and Professor of Dermatology and Mycology at the School of Tropical Medicine, since 1938 (1932, in mycology). Also, he was listed as Instructor in Transmissible Diseases. "Announcement 1926-1927" Archivo Central, UPR. Since 1931, he was associate editor of the School's journal, *Puerto Rico Journal of Public Health and Tropical Medicine*.

36   Ramón M. Suárez, MD (1917, Med. Col. Virginia), internist, cardiologist and Professor at the School of Tropical Medicine, 1928-1949. During O'Connor's visit, he was listed as Assistant Clinical Professor of Tropical Medicine. "Faculty list, 1927-28." Archivo Central, UPR. He conducted research in nutrition and gained prominence by using folic acid the treatment of sprue.

1. A lawyer, Naegles,[37] and his lady secretary, having finished a case which they had come from the U.S. to plead at the local courts, decided on the evening before sailing to have a swim in the sea by moonlight. Soon after entering the water the man saw a large shark. Placing himself between the girl and the monster he fought its fierce rushes for some time, being badly bitten on the thighs, body and arms. Diving past the man and below the girl, the shark tore off the latter's left breast. Finally in an exhausted condition, the mutilated pair reached shore alive and were taken to the hospital, where both nearly died but eventually recovered, the man, however, being seriously crippled for life.

2. A barracuda devoured a child and killed a man who went to her relief (first blinding him by attacking the eyes and nose of the victim).

3. A barracuda disemboweled a man and left little more than shreds of flesh on the skeleton. O'C will not use his bathing suit while in Porto Rico.

We had delicious tropical dainties to eat, including fruit cocktail of papaya, palm pulp salad, and coconut ice cream. R.A.L. had especially ordered these things for the guests' enjoyment, and with characteristic good taste he had also arranged that there were to be no speeches at this first festive gathering.

11 P. M. Back in the hotel. In my blue dressing gown I sat by the window with my feet on the sill and while I drank iced water (tomorrow it will be with whiskey), I looked over the shining waters of the Condado Lagoon to the hills with coconut palms on the ridges silhouetted against the night

---

37   "Naegles," (sic) Neagle, see: Rafael Aponte Ledée. "María la de Utuado: Los orígenes de la plena, segunda parte." *El Nuevo Día*, Revista Domingo, San Juan, 25 Abril 1999: 18-19.

sky, while every now and again lightning on the mountains illuminated the heights, plains and bay. The rain had ceased and peace was everywhere. The frogs were chanting below in the woods and the crickets were chirruping in the bushes.

Tuesday
November 1, 1927.

At 8 A.M. Dr. Oscar Costa Mandry[38] (Associate in Bacteriology) called for me in his car, and drove me out through the Santurce suburb on the eastern road and north aspect[39] of the island to the town of Río Piedras, where we visited the Municipal Health Unit.[40] We met Dr. E. Martínez,[41] who despite a grave family bereavement the day before, received us with characteristic courtesy and explained all the details of his organization. The municipality has a population of 28,094 people, of whom 20,437 are rural, and 7,657 are urban. There are at present two such municipal health units in Porto

---

38   Oscar Costa Mandry, MD (1921, Maryland) with a certificate in tropical medicine (1928, School of Tropical Medicine, UPR). He was one of the first sixteen students registered in the School of Tropical Medicine for its first term (October 1926-January 1927). "Minutes of the Special Board of Trustees of the University of Puerto Rico for the School of Tropical Medicine held May 11, 1927." Archivo Central, UPR. Professor of pathology and bacteriology at the School of Tropical Medicine, since 1927. He was director of the Biological Research Laboratory, Puerto Rico Health Department (1927-1966). (*Quién es Quién en Puerto Rico*, 1933-34, op.cit.: 53-54.)

39   Way of looking, as to position or direction. (*The Oxford English Dictionary*)

40   The Public Health units, which focused on functions rather than specific diseases, were spearheaded in 1925 by Dr. Antonio Fernós Isern, then Assistant Commissioner of Health. From 1926 to 1938, the units were sponsored in part by the Rockefeller Foundation. Ramírez de Arellano, Annette B. "The politics of public health in Puerto Rico: 1926-1940." *Revista de Salud Pública de Puerto Rico*. 3, 1981: 35-54.

41   Dr. Ezequiel Martínez.

Rico, the other being at Yabucoa,[42] and the success attending their administration justifies the hope that other units will be inaugurated throughout the Island in the near future. This unit was started as follows:

1. A conference was held with local doctors to explain the nature and scope of the work to be done.
2. A publicity campaign was then begun by means of the local press, cinemas, lectures, etc., and
3. The unit was established and put in operation to handle:
   a. prevention of disease, and
   b. treatment.

The method of operating the unit is as simple as is consistent with efficiency. The local doctors report to the unit all notifiable diseases on simple cards which are given to them for that purpose. The unit's officers inspect and examine the notified cases to confirm the doctor's findings or otherwise. By this means statistics of reliable nature are collected and epidemiology is studied. The Unit treats all notifiable cases and immunizes all contacts free of charge. With further regard to prevention work, the following are worth noting: All projected sanitary works have to be inspected and construction is not allowed without a permit from the unit. Stores and eating places have to be inspected and may not be opened without a similar permit. All people handling food in eating places have to be examined three times monthly when Wassermanns[43]

---

42   A town in the southeastern region of the island.
43   A serologic test for syphilis.

are done and cultures from throat and faeces are examined. Where there is any infringement of the above laws, the unit prosecutes the offenders directly in the courts. No child can get a permit to go to school without vaccination, and as school is compulsory, all are vaccinated before the age of six at latest. By the simple method of explaining the advantages to the people 35,000 persons have received anti-diphtheritic serum. Self imposed by-laws bind the municipality to contribute ¼ of the expenses of the Unit, but during the year the municipality gave in addition as a free gift $1,000 to install a dental clinic. The clinic does preventive work for children free, but adults must pay. There is also an ante-natal clinic to advise and help expectant mothers.

The officers of the Unit inspect the boarding houses of the students at the University of Porto Rico in Río Piedras. These houses used to be often in an unsuitable condition, but now they are rapidly improving and everyone benefits by these inspections. The owners vie with each other to improve housing conditions in order to get the students. The students become educated in elementary and important health matters and carry the gospel back to their villages and mountain homes.

Several workers from the Unit handle cases of excessive poverty and in addition rich ladies collect funds and hand them to the Unit for distribution.

The Unit carries on a continuous education campaign through the papers, by lectures, and by using the local cinematograph companies. The unit also acts as a training center for would-be sanitarians from other parts of the island,

and especially for those in whose districts it is hoped that eventually units similar to this one, will be put in operation.

Dr. Martínez's staff for all this work is as follows:

1 doctor	}	
3 nurses	}	
4 inspectors	}	full-time
1 secretary	}	
1 social worker	}	
1 janitor	}	
1 inspector of construction	}	
2 doctors	}	part-time
9 nurses	}	
1 clerk	}	

During my visit the clinics of the Unit were crowded but there was no fuss. The obvious success of the Unit is due to several factors—a suitable Director and the enthusiasm of him and of his staff—cooperation of local doctors, and cooperation of the municipality and of managers of local industries—general spirit of the Porto Rican people manifested in many ways to better their condition and acquire education—facility of enforcing legal measures with a people naturally obedient to laws.

Dr. Román Benítez,[44] Assistant to the Director of the

---

44 Manuel Román Benítez (1915, Med. Col. Virginia), also held the position of Assistant Director of the Bureau of Communicable Diseases in the Puerto Rico Department of Health, where he was medical officer for fourteen years.

Giving treatment for hookworm (Photo and comment: F.W. O'Connor)
(Courtesy of the Malloch Rare Book Room of the New York Academy of Medicine Library)

Unit's Hookworm Campaign, met us at the Municipal Health Unit, and when we had finished there, he drove us to Monacillos to see the house-to-house treatment for hookworm.[45] We drove up a little country road and presently came to some very disreputable thatched cabins just off the road and placed in damp boggy surroundings. There, cabins are raised from the ground on corner poles. The interiors are dark and dirty and many showed evidence of overcrowding. The occupants looked ill and undernourished. They were shy but courteous. Román

---

45   Hookworm disease, ankylostomiasis. Infestation with or disease caused by hook-worms; a lethargic anemic state due to blood loss through the feeding of hookworms in the small intestine. (*Medline Plus Medical Dictionary*) Two important species of hook-worms are Necator americanus (American or New World) and Ancylostoma duodenale (Old World). (*Dorland's Pocket*; op. cit.: 329.) In 1989, Dr. Bailey K. Ashford identified hookworm as the cause of a lethal anemia among displaced rural residents in Ponce, Puerto Rico.

Benítez at once offered the medicine, carbon tetrachloride, oil of chenopodium and salts. Sometimes the patients were afraid and R.B.'s patience and quiet firmness were admirable. In every case he got the people to take the treatment. Latrines had been built everywhere. Despite the poverty, the clear spaces around the houses were kept clean and there was no evidence of refuse accumulating. There was some evidence of ambition and love of beauty at each house, as shown by the growing bananas, a few flowers planted and blooming, and the presence of some pigeons. The country people apparently love their birds. Following the treatment, R.B. gave a demonstration concerning hookworm, the mode of infection, its ravages, and its prevention, with large diagrammatic pictures. The interest which the people took in the lecture, their willingness to learn, their quickness in understanding, are encouraging. But their surroundings are depressing and we are glad to return to Río Piedras where we visited for a few minutes the headquarters of the Anti-Hookworm Unit and saw how the work was organized.

On the way back to San Juan my Cicerone drove me through the new residential section named Floral Park between Río Piedras and Santurce. The Park is laid out on the American suburban plan of better class bungalows. But there the resemblance ceases, for there is originality in the architecture of each house which is Spanish or Moorish in design, and each has its own distinct kind of Spanish coloring with picturesque designs of inlay work on pillars and above the arches, etc. The general result is very pleasing to the eye.

Lunch at the Tropical School.

In the afternoon with W.A. Hoffman to the Asilo de

Dormitory in which large numbers of *Culex fatigans* were found on under surface of sheets hanging down over sides of the beds. Some of these mosquitoes were found to contain the fully developed larvae of *Microfilaria bancrofti*, the parasite of Filariasis in Porto Rico. (Photo and comment: F.W. O'Connor)

(Courtesy of the Malloch Rare Book Room of the New York Academy of Medicine Library)

Niños (Boys' Charity School),[46] where W.A.H. had found a fairly high percentage of the boys infected with microfilariae.[47] We visited two of the boys' dormitories and collected mosquitoes (all *Culex*[48] *fatigans*) from these and one from the lavatories. The mosquitoes in the dormitories were all on the undersurface of the sheets hanging down over the beds and never on the walls. This may be due to the fact that there is an ant in Porto Rico

---

46   Established by Cayetano Coll y Toste, while he was civil secretary of General Brigadier George W. Davis, Military Governor of Puerto Rico (1899-1900). Located in the former Jesuit School in Santurce, where the Department of Health still houses some offices. (See *Boletín Histórico de Puerto Rico* 1922, 9: 53-56.)

47   The prelarval stage of Filarioidea in the blood of infected persons and in the tissues of the vector. (*Dorland's Pocket*; op. cit.: 419.)

48   A genus of mosquitoes found throughout the world, many species of which are vectors of disease-producing organisms. (*Dorland's Pocket*; op. cit.: 177.)

which is very active in destroying living larvae and adult flies, and the mosquitoes would be safer under the beds. We took these mosquitoes back to the School where I began dissecting them. I was delighted when I found three fully developed larvae of *Filaria bancrofti* in the head of one mosquito and later when I found a half grown larva in the thorax of another, thus settling the question of the direct transmission of the human filariae for this island.

About 4:30, R.A.L. and I in the car started east through Santurce along a lovely country road, narrowing to a lane and which ended at a little promontory called Boca de Cangrejos (the mouth of the crabs). Following the rains there were big floods at places along the way and some of the native houses were partially submerged. Opposite the Boca de Cangrejos is another promontory with coconut grove where Gilda Gray[49] and her colleagues performed some of the acts for the film, "Aloma of the South Seas," which production gave offence to the Porto Ricans. On the way back to town, we visited a modern dairy farm in the midst of an up-to-date coconut plantation.

6:30 P.M. After dressing, to dinner with Walter A. Glines,[50] one time army man who worked with Dr. Samuel T.

---

49   Gilda Gray (1897-1959), Polish dancer and actress whose first starring role was as a South Seas dancer named Aloma in the American silent film "Aloma of the South Seas" (1926), which was partially shot in Puerto Rico.

50   Walter A. Glines (1906, Maryland), doctor in medicine that practiced the profession in Puerto Rico since 1910. He was once a member of the Junta Insular de Sanidad de Puerto Rico. During O'Connor's visit, he was listed as Resident Lecturer in Medicine at the School of Tropical Medicine. "Faculty list, 1927-28." Archivo Central, UPR.

Darling[51] in Panamá. A very nice house, admirably constructed for the tropics. The main living room, a big library with lots of books, mainly classics. Dr. Glines, a highly cultured person who knows how to enjoy life and apparently does so—an excellent host.

After a preliminary cocktail, not to be forgotten, dinner was served in the patio (or central court garden). The patio contained a profusion of crotons and poinsettias. All these could be seen by moonlight and the reflection of candles on the table. Above an arch at the further end of the patio one saw the grateful slender stem of tall coconut rising to the regal head silhouetted against a tropical night's blue, while between the fronds of the tree in golden brilliance flashed the crescent of the quarter moon. An oriental odor of subtle beauty pervaded the atmosphere; this was familiar to me as from Japan, and I was confirmed in my suspicion when at the request of our host his servant brought from the roof the snow white blossoms of the Japanese "Evening Glory"[52] or "Flor de Luna." To complete the tropical atmosphere, we had soy with our rice, and Turkish coffee, and we lit our cigarettes at candle flame, all of which brought vivid recollections of other parties in other places on verandahs and in tea houses by rivers and by ocean beaches in years gone by.

After dinner we three drove to the Tropical School where I gave my first lecture, semi-scientific and semi-popular,

---

51   Samuel T. Darling, Chief of the Board of Health Laboratory, Isthmian Canal Commission (established in 1904), a distinguished malariologist who conducted research in Panamá and is remembered as a pioneer in the control of malaria during the period.

52   A climbing vine, invasive, with tender blue flowers. The endemic species in Puerto Rico is "morning glory," better known locally as "bejuco de puerco."

on filariasis in Polynesia. There were about 55 persons present, and the affair seemed to go fairly well.

Wednesday,
November 2, 1927.

R.A.L. arrives at my hotel at 8 A.M. and takes me to the Presbyterian Hospital[53] where I went round the wards with Drs. Garry R. Burke and Américo Serra—first in the children's ward—saw many cases of infantile diarrhea and marasmus. It is said that there is no true rickets in Porto Rico. I saw a boy, aged 8 to 10, with pellagra[54] and schistosomiasis.[55] In the adult wards I saw many cases of sprue;[56] some of these were borderline cases, either sprue or pernicious anaemia,[57] and

---

53   Presbyterian Hospital, established in 1904 by a board of women missionaries of the Presbyterian Church; in 1917, the hospital was relocated to its current location in Condado. In 1979, it was renamed Ashford Memorial Community Hospital, in honor of Bailey K. Ashford (in 1984, Ashford Presbyterian Community Hospital). The hospital was one of the "clinical facilities" ("80 beds; distance from School by automobile, 10 minutes") used by the School of Tropical Medicine "for teaching," during O'Connor's visit. "Announcement 1926-1927." Archivo Central, UPR.

54   A disease marked by dermatitis, gastrointestinal disorders, and dementia, and associated with a diet deficient in niacin and protein. I.M. Freedberg, A.Z. Eisen, K. Wolff et al. eds. *Fitzpatrick's Dermatology in General Medicine*, Vol. II, 6th ed. NY: McGraw Hill, 2003: 1405.

55   An infestation with or disease caused by schistosomes. A severe endemic human disease in much of Africa and parts of Asia and Southern America that is caused by worms of the genus Schistosoma which multiply in snail intermediate hosts, are disseminated into freshwaters and bore into the body when it is in contact with infested water. Called also bilharzia or bilharziasis. (*Medline Plus Medical Dictionary*)

56   A disease of tropical regions with unknown cause, is characterized by fatty diarrhea and malabsorption of nutrients. (*Medline Plus Medical Dictionary*)

57   Also, a megaloblastic anemia, an autoimmune disease of insidious onset producing gastric atrophy and impaired intrinsic factor production, resulting in malabsorption of vitamin B12. *Fitzpatrick's Dermatology in General Medicine*, op.cit.: 1528.

some have not been differentiated at all. Though cramps may be bad in Porto Rican sprue, yet tetany[58] and writers' cramp[59] are not seen. I saw a case of bilateral elephantiasis[60] of legs with curious shark skin-like trophic changes on the skin above the toes. There was one case of elephantiasis of the scrotum with no history of lymphangitis[61] or fever. The appendage simply increased in size at intervals. There was also a case of broncho-pneumonia[62] in a child heavily infected with ascaris.

Then back to the Tropical School where before and after lunch I dissected more of my mosquitoes, and I found another positive with larvae in the head of the insect. Later I discussed with Hoffman his filarial survey.

At 4 P.M. Dr. Pedro Ortiz came and with Dr. Taussig,[63] meteorologist, we drove first to the Psychiatric Hospital. This hospital which from every aspect commands beautiful views of vast plains and mountains is constructed on American plans as to practicability, but in appearances is definitely Spanish

---

58   A syndrome manifested by sharp flexion of the wrist and ankle joints, muscle twitchings, cramps, and convulsions. (*Dorland's Pocket*; op. cit.: 673.)

59   An occupational syndrome marked by spasmodic contraction of the muscles of the fingers, hand, and forearm, with neuralgic pain. (*Dorland's Pocket*; op. cit.: 172.)

60   An enlargement and thickening of tissues. The enormous enlargement of a limb or the scrotum caused by obstruction of lymphatics by filarial worms. (*Medline Plus Medical Dictionary*)

61   An inflammation of a lymphatic vessel or vessels. (*Dorland's Pocket*; op. cit.: 395.)

62   A lower respiratory tract infection accompanied by systemic and respiratory tract symptoms.

63   Referent unidentified.

throughout.[64] There are two floors and the several buildings are connected with covered walks bordered by Moorish arches. The whole roof above each building is prepared as a solarium and recreation ground. Though every caution has been taken to prevent escape, there is a minimum appearance of effort to restrain the patients. The institution is capable of housing 1,000 patients and will care for all psychiatric cases in the Island. Good equipment has been installed for preventive as well as for curative treatment. The wards are constructed to hold 4 or 10 beds each; but never two in case one patient should become violent with another; the larger numbers allow for observation by other patients. The building is placed on an elevation in spacious grounds and away from the disturbing influence of main thoroughfares. The institution is not yet in operation.[65] From the Psychiatric Hospital we drove about 200 yards to the entrance of the Tuberculosis Sanatorium.[66] The latter has been functioning for about two years. We drove along an avenue bordered by stately royal palms and shrubs of variegated colors. The public wards are placed at short distance back from the drive on either side, and are so arranged that

---

64   For the paradoxes inherent in Spanish Revival architecture in Puerto Rico, see: Rigau, Jorge. *Puerto Rico 1900*. New York: Rizzoli, 1992, esp. Ch. 5, "Spanish Revival as Spanish denial": 177-209; and Vivoni Farage, Enrique and Álvarez Curbelo, Silvia eds. *Hispanofilia/Hispanophilia: Architecture and Life in Puerto Rico*, 1900-1950. San Juan: Editorial de la Universidad de Puerto Rico, 1998.

65   In 1923, the Puerto Rico Legislature approved the building of the Psychiatric Hospital, but its construction was not completed until 1929. Roselló, J.A. *Historia de la Psiquiatría Puertorriqueña*. San Juan: IRHI, 1988: 13.

66   The Tuberculosis Sanitarium, a special hospital of the Health Department, was one of the clinical facilities ("200 beds; distance from School by automobile, 30 minutes") used by the School of Tropical Medicine for clinical instruction, during O'Connor's visit. "Announcement 1926-1927." Archivo Central, UPR.

two patients only occupy each ward. In these rooms there is a window space on each side and facing the drive there is a spacious verandah. All beds are movable and patients can roll them without effort onto the verandah, where there is ample room for them and where they may sleep when weather permits. The women's wards are on one side of the drive and the men's on the other. Patients are disciplined on arriving at the Sanatorium about spitting, and it was remarkable that during my visit there was no coughing. There are also some private buildings for patients who are capable of paying and desire more privacy. All buildings are placed at some distance from each other and very pretty gardens and green plots surround each of these. The institution is full to capacity and many cases of tuberculosis are unable to get entrance. The discharge of patients is complicated by the fact that the patients are very opposed to leaving, and this is not surprising when one sees the beauty of the place and the comfort and freedom in which the patients live in this garden city. All milk for the patients is provided by a model tropical dairy in the premises. The cows are of the Jersey breed and they are protected from Texas fever by dipping.[67] The dairy is cared for by convicts who are also responsible for the upkeep of the grounds, etcetera.

The sun was setting as we left the Sanatorium and it was dusk as we drove along the road to San Juan. It was Halloween[68] and we met throngs of people walking towards a cemetery carrying flowers and candles. When we came to the cemetery it was crowded with people attending to the graves,

---

67   The ticks that transmit Texas cattle fever are eliminated when the cow is "dipped," or passed through a trough full of an insecticide-containing solution.
68   O'Connor must be referring to "Día de los muertos" or All Saints Day (November 2), not Halloween (October 31).

placing their flowers, and lighting their candles, hundreds of which flickering in the gloom made an impressive effect. A pretty old Spanish custom this.

Shortly after my return to the hotel, R.A.L. arrived and drove Mr. Mansfield of New Haven (friend of R.A.L.) and me for dinner at the Union Club. W.A. Hoffman joined the party. After dinner R.A.L. took us to his rooms and on the verandah gave us a delightful lantern slide demonstration of his colored photograph slides of tropical flowers in Brazil and Porto Rico, including flamboyant and bougainvillea. Later we drove to the Presbyterian Hospital where I recovered my notebook which I had left there in the morning.

Ortiz tells me that there are not many cases of violence such as murder, etc. in the Island.

Thursday,
November 3, 1927.

A bright day of sunshine. At 8 A.M. started with W.A.H. and Mr. Marín[69] and with Jenaro at the wheel for Guayama on the South Coast. Circling the margins of the Condado Lagoon, we entered the lower range of foot hills of the interior. We drove along the old Spanish military road which, like most of the roads in Porto Rico, is admirably constructed, and level, being covered with ferro concrete. We passed a bullock wagon, and one cannot help feeling that the method of harnessing

---

69   There is a Rafael Ángel Marín, BS (1923, Harvard), listed as Assistant in Parasitology at the School of Tropical Medicine. "Faculty, 1927-28." Archivo Central, UPR. Also, a "Mr. Marin" appears as an assistant to Dr. William A. Hoffman in a review of research carried out at the School (1926-28) by Dr. Robert A. Lambert. *Porto Rico Review of Public Health and Tropical Medicine*, 1928, 4 (3): 107-116: 108.

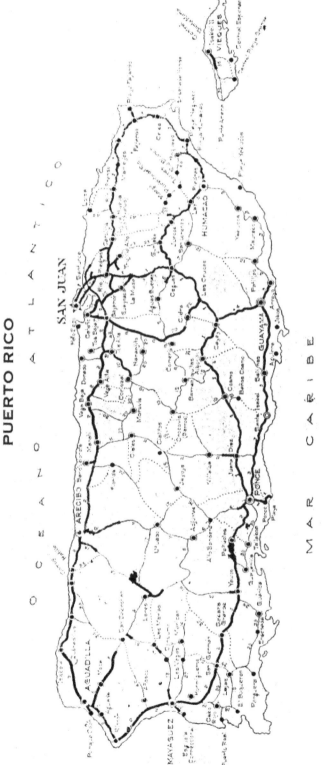

MAPA ITINERARIO DE LAS CARRETERAS INSULARES

DE

PUERTO RICO

Road Map of Puerto Rico, Government of Puerto Rico, Department of the Interior, Bureau of Public Works, 1928

these poor animals with a heavy beam above and connecting their heads is cruel. The soft patient eyes of the beasts look rather pathetic. Coconut palms became scarcer as we traveled inland, but the tall straight royal palms with dark green fronds and greyish white stems added considerably to the beauty of the undulating hills. After about ¾ hours we descended to a plain and passed through the typically Spanish town of Caguas. Here we saw the Plaza with its church, the buildings mostly one storied of bright colors and with a predominance of bright yellow, Portuguese blue, green and browns (burnt sienna), always against white. But despite the brilliance, the colors seemed in harmony with the surroundings and never impressed one as being gaudy. This may be in part because the architecture is always so simple and subdued. The people are particularly handsome in the main and dark with large gentle eyes. Many go barefoot and the women show a preference for bright orange and green dresses which contrast pleasingly with the brunette types. These people never stare at one like so many other natives. They are courteous in making salutations and in answering questions and under ordinary circumstances they strike one as quiet and peaceful. Leaving the town we ascended to the central range of hills and saw the young tobacco being planted on the hill slopes where during its early tender weeks it is protected by mosquito netting. Reaching higher altitudes coffee was seen growing in every available place, the green and pinkish berries being well developed in size. The dark red blooms of the hibiscus, so common in the plains, were rarer and now began to give place to light pink ones which grow better in the cooler climate. There are many sharp turns in the mountain roads and at each one a new vista of valleys and hills was enjoyed; the dark red clay of the newly ploughed

Bullock cart carrying cane (Photo and comment: F.W. O'Connor)
(Courtesy of the Malloch Rare Book Room of the New York Academy of Medicine Library)

fields on the mountain slopes make a brilliant contrast with the dark and lighter greens of adjoining woods and growing crops. There was ample evidence of the industry of the rural population in the fact that every available piece of ground, even up to 2,300 feet and often higher, was under cultivation. Having reached the higher points of the road we began a long descent down the winding road to the wood plain wherein is placed the town of Cayey and the United States military and wireless stations. There are numerous tobacco storehouses in the plain. After crossing the plain from north to south, we again began to ascend, this time to an altitude of 2,000 feet. On the 35 mile stretch of road, including ascent and descent, there are 300 sharp curves. From the highest point we had a view of range after range of mountains and hills descending toward a great plain with tidy cane fields in the midst of which the white houses of the city of Guayama flashed clear against the surrounding light green mountains which bordered each side of the plains, and beyond and between the mountains, one saw the sapphire blue of the Caribbean. On this journey we passed the Governor's summer residence—one of the old Spanish rest houses of one story constructed of red brick—an unpretentious house for a high official but commanding an unrivalled view of the mountains, valleys and sea in the distance. As we began the descent, the vista in front reminded me of the scenes in Greece, where emerging from below Parnassus I first beheld the blue of the Corinthian Gulf. Reaching the plain we soon arrived at Guayama, headquarters of the Machete Sugar Central, and turning to the right out of the town we drove half a mile to a small native house in a sugar plantation where Schistosomiasis is prevalent. We went to one of the irrigation ditches where W.A.H. originally found *Planorbis guadaloupensis*[70] infected with *Schistosoma mansoni*.[71] The irrigation channels are made of brick, while beside them are ditches to which are allowed to flow under control of sluices sufficient water for the different plots. Those ditches also act as drains to carry off flood water from the plantation. In both kinds of channels, but especially in the latter, *Planorbis* abound in large numbers. The snails tend to lie on the bottom of the ditches when the water is clear, but they come to the surface when it is muddy, as after rains. The people not only enter the water with bare feet to clean the ditches at intervals, but the children as well as adults bathe in these waters.

---

70   A freshwater snail that serves as a natural host for the parasitic blood fluke (flattened shape), Schistosoma mansoni.

71   A genus of trematodes (flatworms)—Schistosoma, commonly known as blood-flukes and bilharzias. See Note 55.

Persons so engaged complain that they suffer from severe itch while in the water and that sometimes this becomes so intolerable that they have to leave the water. They can distinguish between the itch so caused and that due to hookworm infection, and they have distinct Spanish names for each kind of itch.[72] I saw several of the occupants of the neighboring house who looked very ill. They were anaemic and lacking in stamina.

At 12:30 P.M. we lunched at the Hotel de Paris in the town (fried chicken). Then we started for San Juan, returning by the same route. The distance from San Juan to Guayama is 70 miles and thus we had travelled 140 miles when we arrived back in San Juan.

We had left San Juan at 8:30. Arrived Guayama 12 P. M.

We had left Guayama at 1:30. Arrived San Juan 3:40 P.M.

The outward journey took longer owing to frequent stops so that I could take photographs.

At 4:10, R.A.L. took me to call on Mrs. Towner, the Governor's[73] wife, at Government House, Palacio de Santa Catalina or La Fortaleza, built in 1540. It has a picturesque Moorish entry and tower, and there is a strange cylindrical column on the roof terminating in a vertical four sided sundial constructed in the 16th century. The patio is full of many colored crotons and beautiful flowers. Mrs. Towner let us inspect the

---

72   "Piquiña" (a common term for itch) in schistosomiasis (Pons, Juan A. "Estudios sobre la esquistosomiasis de Manson en Puerto Rico. V. Aspectos clínicos." *PR Journal of Public Health and Tropical Medicine* 1937-38; 13: 255-349, esp. 273); mazamorra (a rural term for itch or disease between the toes or hooves) in hookworm infection (Ashford Bailey K. "The larval phase of uncinariasis." *PR Journal of Public Health and Tropical Medicine* 1933-34; 9: 97-134, esp. 97; and Álvarez Nazario, Manuel. *El habla campesina del País*. San Juan: Edit. Universidad de Puerto Rico, 1990: 371). The editors thank Dr. George V. Hillyer for identifying the term "piquiña".

73   Horace Mann Towner was a lawyer and the Congressman (1911-23) named Governor of Puerto Rico by President Calvin Coolidge (both served, 1923-29).

building from the roof from which we had a fine view of the bay and surrounding country. As we looked at the basement, cellars and its forbidding dungeon doors, one could not help reflecting on the misery of the inmates at periods in the past. We had tea with Mrs. Towner and then we went to see the old Spanish Gate of the City.

Dined with R.A.L. at the Union Club and later we went to the Tropical School where we heard C. Weiss[74] lecture on antigens and lipoids. Then R.A.L. conducted a clinico-pathological conference which included cases of leprosy[75] and malaria. W.C. Earle[76] gave an excellent discourse on the difficulties attending the diagnosis of malaria. It was very refreshing to hear Earle, after careful studies, calmly critical and unwilling to accept all the unproven dogmatisms of recent writers. He has read considerably and made many useful observations himself, and if given opportunity and as free a hand as possible should do useful work, if he does not get discouraged. He is sceptical about the universal application of the splenic index.[77] I supported Earle in the discussion with a

---

74   Charles Weiss, Ph.D, MD (1924, Penn.), appeared on a list of salaried appointments to the School of Tropical Medicine, for the year July 1927-June 1928, as Assistant Professor of Bacteriology. "Minutes of the Special Board of Trustees of the University of Puerto Rico for the School of Tropical Medicine held May 11, 1927." Archivo Central, UPR. He published several research articles on tropical sprue in Puerto Rico.

75   Hansen disease is a chronic condition caused by infection with a bacillus (Mycobacterium leprae) and characterized by the formation of nodules on the surface of the body and especially on the face or by the appearance of tuberculoid macules on the skin. (*Medline Plus Medical Dictionary*)

76   Walter C. Earle, MD (1920, Rush, Chicago), Instructor in Malaria and Malaria Prevention at the School of Tropical Medicine. "Faculty list, 1927-28." Archivo Central, UPR.

77   A measure of the size of the spleen in patients afflicted by malaria.

few words. W.A.H presented me with some Haigh and Haigh[78] and the Burkes took me for a drive and later took me to the Condado Vanderbilt.

Friday,
November 4, 1927.

R.A.L. drove me to the Municipal Hospital, an old building in Santurce. It is picturesque, being white and blue, but it lacks many modern conveniences. Here we were met by Dr. José Ferrer, the surgeon, who has been very kind and cooperative in collecting cases for me to see, and Dr. A. Martínez Álvarez, the internist. Dr. Ferrer showed us round the wards and then we saw several cases of filariasis, and some cases of elephantiasis, including one of a boy of 13, with elephantiasis of the left leg which I photographed. We also saw some cases of hydrocele.[79] I was told of cases of bubonic plague[80] causing a cessation of filarial attacks.

Next we drove back through San Juan to the Bureau of Plague Prevention where Dr. Arturo L. Carrión gave freely of his time and explained in detail the work of the Bureau. Two kinds of rat traps used: cage traps...and snap traps.[81] The

---

78   Blended Scotch whiskey from Scotland.
79   A circumscribed collection of fluid, especially around the testis or along the spermatic cord. (*Dorland's Pocket*; op. cit.: 331.)
80   An acute febrile infection caused by a bacterium (Yersinia pestis) transmitted by the bite of the flea of rodents. Enlarged, inflamed, painful lymph nodes, called buboes (most commonly in the groin, armpits or neck) give bubonic plague its name. As O'Connor later indicates, plague was epidemic in Puerto Rico in 1912 (55 cases, including 36 deaths) and 1921 (20 deaths in 33 cases) and disappeared thereafter.
81   Technical comment in the original, displaced to this footnote: "Cage traps distributed as 300 a day, 250 a day, and so on, estimating the numbers caught in the traps 9 + in 1,000 traps. Snap traps 12 + for 75 No. per 1,000."

traps are baited with ripe coconut. The chief tree rat is the *Mus norwegicus*[82] which can cross telegraph wires. For collecting fleas cage traps are used. The work is only being done in San Juan at present owing to lack of funds for extending work to other parts, and San Juan is the place most exposed to danger. The two recent epidemics of 1912 and 1921 began in San Juan. Infection came from Spain. The mongoose[83] is also a trouble in the Island. It was brought in to deal with the rat. It failed to do so and has become a pest (O'C. recalls the same circumstances in Mauritius and Lafcadio Hearn[84] describes it in the French West Indies.)

The annual budget for the work is $20,000, a decrease from $40,000. The 1912 epidemic cost $350,000 (55 cases). The 1921 cost $500,000 (33 cases). Carrión showed us different rats:

Mus alexandrinus—small, white belly, smooth long tail.
Mus norwegicus—large, black belly, short rough tail.
Mus rattus—like *Alexandrinus*, but black belly.

For detecting chronic carriers amongst rats, C. makes emulsion of material from spleen and injects 1 c.c. subcutaneously into guinea pigs.

The ordinary test of routine cases is made by shaving and scrubbing abdomen of pig and smearing with spleen or liver of the rat.

---

82   The former name for Rattus norvegicus.

83   A small to medium size, long-tailed carnivore rodent from Africa, Southern Europe, and Asia brought to Puerto Rico from Jamaica by a Mr. William Lamb, in 1877. Colón, E.D. *Datos sobre la agricultura de Puerto Rico antes de 1898.* San Juan: Cantero, Fernández, Co., 1930: 261.

84   Lafcadio Hearn (1850-1904), American author born in the Greek Island of Lefkas that was educated in Ireland, England and France. As a literary translator he was assigned by a publisher to the West Indies, from 1887 to 1889, and wrote two novels on that period. Afterwards, he moved to Japan where he wrote most of his literary works.

The Chigger flea, *Echinodefaga gallinacea*, also occurs in the Island. Most of the fleas found on the Porto Rico rats are *Xenopsylla cheopis*. C. showed me how he took living rats from cage with forceps, broke their necks and suspended them over water in broad basin, nose down, to catch the fleas.

To the Tropical School for lunch and then with W. A.H. to the Asilo de Niños to collect more mosquitoes. In the dormitories previously inspected by us there were no mosquitoes but in another we had not visited before we found lots of mosquitoes. Back to the School and I dissected some of the insects but found none positive. At 4:30 P.M. attended lecture on legal medicine by Dr. Antonio Fernós Isern. After the lecture more dissecting till 6 P.M. when R.A.L. took me to Dr. D.H. Cook's for dinner. Dr. and Mrs. Earle, and W.A.H. also present. A very pleasant party. At 8:30, W.A.H. and I left to join Dr. Alice Burke[85] and Marín at the Asilo de Niños to examine night blood of the younger boys. The boys are well disciplined and appear to be well cared for and in good condition. They were taken from their beds and paraded in pairs before us, but we found only one positive in 30 of the younger children. Demonstrated to W.A.H. a simple method of taking and examining blood which he is inclined to adopt.

---

85   Alice M.B. Burke, MD (1918, Buffalo), was one of the first sixteen students registered in the School of Tropical Medicine for its first term (October 1926-January 1927). Also, Burke appeared on a list of salaried appointments to the School of Tropical Medicine, for July 1927-June 1928, as Instructor in Clinical Pathology. "Minutes of the Special Board of Trustees of the University of Puerto Rico for the School of Tropical Medicine held May 11, 1927." Archivo Central, UPR. In a review of research carried out at the School of Tropical Medicine during its first two years (1926-28), Dr. Robert A. Lambert states that "Dr. [Alice] Burke is also investigating, with Dr. O'Connor, other clinical manifestations of filariasis." *Porto Rico Review of Public Health and Tropical Medicine*, 1928, 4 (3): 107-116: 108.

A violent thunderstorm was in progress when Dr. Garry Burke came and drove me back to my hotel.

Saturday,
November 5, 1927.

Mail from New York and many nice letters for me. To the School, where I prepared my lecture and also spent some time dissecting mosquitoes. All negative. At 11:30 clinic on a child with ascaris infection and bronchitis.[86] This was presented by Américo Serra, and I then discussed the complications of ascaris based on the study of the literature. R.A.L. described 5 cases from Saõ Paulo, one a case of acute pancreatitis[87] cured by removing the ascaris, and two with biliary cirrhosis.[88] Dr. Costa described a case of lung ascaris simulating glanders.[89]

After lunch, R.A.L. and I with Jenaro started for Coamo Spring, traveling via Bayamón, Comerío, Barranquitas, and Coamo. A very pleasant drive during which we ascended to 2,300 feet from which we could see the sea towards the south. In the earlier part of the journey we passed pineapple plantations on the lowlands, and as we ascended, there were many tobacco and coffee plantations to be seen. Between Comerío and Barranquitas we had a superb view over the valley of the La Plata, and in the distance could see Cayey.

---

86   An inflammation of one or more bronchi. (*Dorland's Pocket*; op. cit.: 111.)

87   An inflammation of the pancreas. (*Dorland's Pocket*; op. cit.: 516.)

88   Cirrhosis of the liver from chronic bile retention. (*Dorland's Pocket*; op. cit.: 151.)

89   A contagious disease of horses, communicable to humans, and marked by purulent inflammation of the mucous membranes and cutaneous eruption of nodules. (*Dorland's Pocket*; op. cit.: 298.)

Tobacco is planted in Porto Rico in October and November and is reaped in April and May. Most of the product is used for fillings for cigars.

On crossing the Divide,[90] one became conscious of different vegetation than that in other places, and here there is a much lower rainfall than elsewhere. The royal palm gets scarce and the flamboyant (of the acacia family) which blooms so brilliantly in July and August is very plentiful, the trees being planted at regular distances of about 20 feet on both sides of the mountain roads near the lower levels. Coamo is a pretty town with brightly colored Spanish houses. Los Baños de Coamo (Coamo Springs)[91] was a revelation to me. I expected to see a modern hotel and was agreeably surprised to find myself exploring an Old World garden and approaching a large two-story Spanish building of early nineteenth century design and of salmon pink colors with white bordering to windows and doors. Set against the dark green of the trees surrounded by multi-colored crotons and poinsettias, the effect is very beautiful. The main hotel is on a slight elevation and therefrom by a covered way one reaches another long one-story building of similar appearance, placed at the foot of a hill with gigantic boulders and densely wooded. This building contains the baths which are supervised by an old woman. The baths are in small rooms mostly containing one bath, oblong structures like a grave with tiled floors and brick sides. The plugs are

90   The Divide is the highest edge of the Central Mountain range of Puerto Rico (Cordillera Central), which divides the wet north from the semi-arid south part of the island, or the point after which the waters flow south instead of north.
91   Thermal springs noted for their healing and therapeutic waters. Los Baños de Coamo, a parador (hostelry) surrounds the famous springs and it was considered one of the island's most fashionable resorts from 1847 to 1958.

made of wood. There are other rooms containing two baths for married couples. The water smells strongly of sulphur, and is of a pleasantly warm temperature, not too hot. The baths have been known for centuries and people came to bathe in water which bubbles out of the spring in the neighboring hill. But the present buildings were only erected 102 years ago by slaves under the Spanish rulers. The reception rooms are typically Spanish, the chairs being arranged in two rows facing each other down the center of the room. In the dining room the women sit on one side of the table, the men being on the other, and where husband and wife are in a party they are placed next to each other. After a refreshing bath we had a very good dinner, and then R.A.L. and I sat on the verandah at the back of the house in the light of the room while the crickets chirruped. It was delightfully cool, although the place is only 100 feet above sea level, and no mosquitoes worried us. R.A.L. told me about his experiences in Venezuela. And so to bed!

Sunday,
November 6, 1927.

At Los Baños de Coamo. For ventilation purposes the rooms of the hotel have no regular doors, and privacy is assured by Venetian swing doors. Consequently the would-be sleeper is forced to hear all that goes on in the hotel lounge. I heard a party in their cups discuss everything from sugar cane to love, till 1 A.M. when they retired and let me sleep. R.A.L.'s more adjustable conscience allowed him to sleep at once despite the noise.

After breakfast, I found a corner in the garden near the baths where there is a pretty pink Spanish gate with vines hanging over the top and a clinging to the sides. Arranging my

Old Spanish gateway at Coamo Springs (Photo and comment: F.W. O'Connor)
(Courtesy of the Malloch Rare Book Room of the New York Academy of Medicine Library)

painting materials, I spent a very pleasant morning attempting to make a sketch. The Porto Rican bath lady brought me a chair to sit on and she and Jenaro and sundry children came from time to time to watch my progress and criticize my efforts. By and by Jenaro led me up the hill behind the baths to see the springs where we found the bubbling water "muchos caliente" [*sic*] as it emerged from the rocks.

Lunch at 12 and when finished we started on the return journey to San Juan. On reaching the main road we turned sharp to the left and on fine roads bordered by flamboyant trees we drove to Ponce and then across the mountains via Adjuntas and Utuado to Arecibo on the North Coast. Though the flamboyant usually only blooms in July and August, I was lucky in seeing one tree in full glory of its bloom and I have never seen anything so brilliant and lovely before. This late blooming may have been due to the continuance of the heat and the heavy rains beyond the usual season. Each flower has three deep orange petals, a fourth petal is often snow white with crimson spots. During one part of the journey we were as high as 2,300 feet. On one of the roads we found almost obstructing the way a boulder of about ten tons' weight which had slid from the mountain. Men were preparing to remove this by dynamite. The sliding of such boulders from the mountain sides after rains is of quite common occurrence. The route took us through a succession of banana plantations and at Arecibo, under the administration of the Soller and Arecibo Centrals is the largest cultivation of sugar I have yet seen in the Island. In the mountains there were numbers of giant tree ferns, the absence of which I had noticed on other routes, and again near the mountain homes were pink hibiscus and a blue convolvulus which I had not previously noticed, while some gardens had masses of variegated colia. Approaching Utuado the road was very tortuous with sharp turns as on the road to Guayama. W.A.H. has found schistosoma at Utuado, although the few *Planorbis* found did not contain cercariae.[92] It is interesting to note in this connection that Utuado is 1,000 feet above sea level. (O'C. There may be another intermediary host in this region). R.A.L. says that it seems that there are more ankylostomes and other intestinal parasites in the inhabitants of Utuado than in any other part of the Island studied up to date.

Notes made during talk with R.A.L. en route.

Agriculturists are 75% of the population in rural

---

92   The larval form of the parasite liberated from the snail intermediate host for all trematode parasites.

districts and there are 381 persons to the square mile. Increase of population is most evident in the coastal belt, although the usual population elsewhere is not decreasing. There is great enthusiasm for education, and schools, urban and rural, are to be seen everywhere. Many of the mountain people dispense with the marriage ceremony and just live together. The argument is that religious marriage is too expensive. Many married men have mistresses and the illegitimate birth rate is high. These children are called "natural children."

I have noticed that most of the fowl in Porto Rico are of the game breed, although a few Plymouth rocks and white leghorns are seen. Cats are not markedly in evidence and dogs are not more numerous than in other countries. One does not notice many wild birds and those seen are not of striking plumage, and I heard no song birds. The pigs are of a poor type. They are, however, a great delicacy, the Porto Ricans say, "Every Saint has his day and every pig has his Saturday." Feasts are given and pig is eaten, "Lechón asado."[93]

Before reaching Arecibo the configuration of the land attracts attention. One sees mountains tops jutting up from the plains. They are of limestone formation due to elevations from the sea.[94] The sea round Porto Rico is said to be deeper than in other parts of the world.[95] These limestone peaks have precipitous sides facing each other across the valleys. They contain many caves in which human bones and relics of the Stone Age have been found.

---

93 Roasted pork.

94 Karst region of Puerto Rico. For more detail see: http://capp.water.usgs.gov/gwa/ch_n/gif/N097.gif.

95 O'Connor refers to the Puerto Rico Trench—an oceanic trench located on the boundary between the Caribbean Sea and the Atlantic Ocean (see: http://en.wikipedia.org/wiki/Puerto_Rico_Trench).

On the outward journey we traveled 60 miles to Los Baños de Coamo and on the return we drove 120: thus during two days we traveled 180 miles by car. We arrived back at San Juan at 7 P.M. On reaching the hotel I found a man called Billing awaiting me with regard to a cure (certain) for tuberculosis. I referred him to R.A.L.

Monday,
November 7, 1927.

<u>Fajardo</u>

At 7:30 with Dr. W. C. Earle drove to Fajardo at the northeast corner of the Island and there at the Municipal Hospital we first watched R.A.L. do a postmortem on a case—female—(2. [Secondary?] syphilitic cirrhosis).

W.C. Earle while driving told me that *Anopheles*[96] *albimanus* is the principal malarial carrier in the Island, other carriers being *A. grabhami* and *A. vestitipennis*. *A. albimanus* is a prolific breeder and breeds in most kinds of water, and will stand a salinity of 2%. It is not a house mosquito and apparently returns to the cane sugar and the trunks for shelter. It bites early in the evening and all night till dawn. The larvae are found in water of cane plantations, mangrove swamps, tins, etc. It can stand a lot of light and breeds all the year round, but is most numerous between September and January. *A. vestitipennis* is most prevalent from December to January. Malaria is prevalent all year round. Parasite ratio generally, *Plasmodium vivax* 2, *P.*

---

96   A widely distributed genus of mosquitoes, comprising over 300 species, many of which are vectors of malaria. (*Dorland's Pocket*; op. cit.: 43.)

Laborers quarters amidst the canefields, and breeding grounds of the *Anopheles albimanus*
(Photo and comment: F.W. O'Connor)
(Courtesy of the Malloch Rare Book Room of the New York Academy of Medicine Library)

falciparum 1, but this year's ratio is reversed.[97] *P. vivax* all the year round but highest incidence October to January.

The Fajardo Sugar Central has a big malaria problem. Vast plains at sea level thickly planted with sugar cane. Difficulty is in necessary opening and shutting of sluices at proper times to control drainage. Laborers' houses without any protection in groups here and there in the midst of the plantations and the breeding places. Near the coast the people are similarly exposed near the mangrove swamps. We visited many breeding places and areas where humans herd and everywhere the conditions were the same—bad.

---

97   O'Connor erroneously took down the information given by Earle when he noted the parasite ratio. According to José G. Rigau-Pérez in his essay, "The Apogee of Tropical Medicine", Earle recognized that *P. falciparum* was in general more frequent than *P. vivax*; the reverse was true only from May to August.

Lunch with R.A.L. at Fajardo Sugar Central.

W.C.E. showed me two modest offices. Here he has made the best with his materials. Three technicians, one of whom being expert, checks the others. W.C.E.'s technique is good. Excellent thick and thin films on one slide. Method of staining slides in bulk excellent. Many slides are fixed by a rubber band, each separated from the other by a piece of thin cardboard, and so the collections are put through filming, staining and washing with minimum waste materials. The results are excellent.

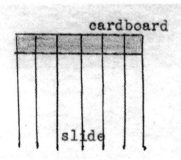

The precipitin method for examining mosquitoes is as follows:

1. Recently fed mosquitoes are squashed on filter paper.
2. Each stained piece when dry is cut out and placed in a dish.
3. Saline is added: the dishes let stand 1 hour or longer.

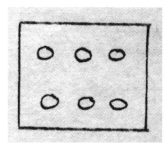

4. A rack of test tubes is taken with the serum one is going to use, man, horse, ox, etc.
5. The tubes are filled with anti-serum till round ends are covered.
6. The mixture (3) is added till a ring is formed above (5). This should be added carefully to avoid moving (3-4 MM.[98]).
7. Read every 10 minutes up to half an hour. Reaction is shown to be positive by a cloud at the meeting of the mixtures.

I collected many *C. fatigans* larvae from a seep near one of the laborers' groups of houses and took them back to San Juan for my culture experiments.

R.A.L. did two more postmortems today. An amazingly conscientious worker—difficult to get him to leave off for lunch.

A pleasant drive back to San Juan. At one spot we saw a mongoose cross the road. On return to San Juan found a big mail awaiting me—all well. Dressed and went to the School

---

98   Meaning unclear; perhaps indicating one adds only 3-4 milimeters of fluid to the tube.

where I gave my lecture on Filariasis—bigger audience than last time. Interesting audience to speak to. Was asked many useful questions afterwards. Home at 11 P.M.

Tuesday,
November 8, 1927.

To office at School. Examined hydrocele fluids and dissected mosquitoes. Then to Río Piedras to see Dr. Henry T. Doermann, Acting Chancellor of the University of Porto Rico, who showed us over the buildings. The Institution is coeducational and at present has more girls than boys. The Porto Rican is not a sticker at work—works in spurts. Boys good in elementary classes but in higher grades most of the exceptional students and prize winners are girls. Male inferiority may be due to nature of sex life. Not much inclination of girls or boys to study music. Altogether the boys seem to lack character.

Doermann was on the stage for a time and while at Harvard acted for sometime with Forbes Robertson[99] in Hamlet taking on some occasions the part of the King.

Back to hotel to pack and later to lunch at the School and there at 2 P.M. started in Ortiz's car with R.A.L. and Garry Burke, and driven by Ortiz's chauffer, for Ponce. We travelled on the same road as on a former trip to Caguas and Cayey, passing the place inland 20 miles where the grove of coconuts is <u>not</u> thriving. But here we took the road to the right instead of the left and traveling along the Valley of the

---

99   Sir Johnston Forbes-Robertson (1853-1937), English actor considered the greatest Hamlet of his age.

La Plata gradually ascended the mountains on the left of the Valley. As we ascended the scenery became more and more beautiful. The mountains are steep and the tobacco laborers seemed to be standing parallel to the mountain sides as they planted the seed. The soil is dark and the innumerable white or gray tobacco barns stand out in marked contrast from this background. The road we travelled is in many places cut right out of the rock, and there are steep cliffs below. The Spaniards guarded the cliff edges by spaced cement parapets. There are numerous sharp, hidden curves on this road. Presently we arrived at Aibonito (How Pretty) which well deserves its name.[100] A very picturesque town at an elevation of 2,000 feet and commanding splendid panoramas in all directions. This is a favorite summer resort of the wealthier people of the Island and there are a large number of pretty residences in well cared for grounds in different parts of the suburbs. At a sharp turn near the town where cars "must" for safety sake slow down, a knowing little mountain *señorita* was waiting to sell "Fraises"[101] or the large wild strawberries of the hills. She climbed up to the car and R.A.L. bought a large basket for 25 cents. Delicious fruit. Then on to Coamo and so by the old route to Ponce. Passing through the town, we ascended a hill on the west to St. Luke's Hospital[102] and here we left my lantern slides. Then we descended and finding a very rough, but the only available road up the mountain behind the town, we ascended for about 700 feet till we came out on the plateau above the city. The sun

---

100 The name is derived from a Puerto Rico native place name, not from the expression "¡Ay, [que] bonito!" as O'Connor states.

101 "Fraises" in French; in Spanish, "fresas."

102 A non-profit missionary institution established in 1906 by the Episcopal Church, known locally as "Hospital San Lucas," still in operation.

was setting behind us, a carmine sphere, producing a variety of reds and golds in the neighboring clouds, and many shades of blues and purples fading to amethyst in the mountains. At the same time, to our left the great full November moon rose stately, a massive golden globe, above a violet ridge in a setting of the deepest blue. Immediately below us and spread out more than a mile in all directions is the City of Ponce, a city of salmon pink houses broken here and there by the deeper greens of mango trees and the lighter shades of the acacias. In the subdued lights of dusk even the tin roofs in the poorer quarters assumed heliotrope tints.[103] Around the town, we admired the grayish greens of the vast cane fields at evening and in the distance the soft blue of the peaceful Caribbean with little coffin island[104] and the twinkly light of its light house, a sentinel in the roadstead. As it grew darker the roofs became redder, while the surrounding colors began gradually to fuse, and then suddenly and simultaneously all the lamps in the streets were lighted. The effect was remarkable, and the scene became oriental in beauty, emphasized by the stillness at our position on the mountain, from where we could hear none of the sounds of the city below.

We descended to the city and drove to the Hotel Meliá, a typically Spanish hotel of two floors, the rooms leading by Venetian doors to a verandah above the street which is bordered by acacia trees, the tops of which reach nearly to the verandah floor. The building is square and surrounds a tiled patio of large dimensions containing tall trees and low shrubs of many colors. After dressing

---

103   This is a moderate, light, or brilliant violet to deep reddish or grayish purple color.
104   "Coffin Island"—O'Connor seems to be translating the name in Spanish: "Caja de Muertos."

and dining, Dr. Rafael López Nussa[105] called for us and we drove to St. Luke's hospital where we found about 150 people gathered, including 35 doctors, all of whom with the exception of about 15 from Ponce had come from towns in the hills, some as far as 45 miles away. There were also the nursing staff and social workers. I lectured on filariasis for about an hour—easy going to an obviously interested audience. When I sat down one of the nurses came forward and presented me with an enormous bouquet of beautiful and sweet scented flowers. This bouquet was a work of art and must have taken much time and trouble to prepare. Then Miss Hicks, the superintendent, gave a reception to which everyone was invited, and I spoke to many doctors and social workers, including some English girls. After an hour, Drs. López and Goyco took R.A.L. and Burke and me to the Casino Club,[106] one of the most luxurious clubs I have been in. It has a gorgeous ball room. We drank champagne in the smoking room, and talked for about an hour. Then at 12:35 we returned to our hotel and I took my bouquet to my room.

Today on the journey, I saw many cattle grazing by the road sides. Cattle graze out of doors all the year round. Amongst the people of Porto Rico, to the ordinary traveler, there is a noticeable absence of eye infections and one rarely

---

105 Rafael López Nussa, MD (1906, Georgetown) was director (1907-1920) of the Ponce Municipal Hospital, Hospital Valentín Tricoche, established in 1876, and of St. Luke's Hospital (Hospital San Lucas), since 1918. The San Juan Municipal Hospital is named after him.

106 An exclusive social civic club built in 1922, French style, designed by architect Agustín Camilo González, located at the intersection of Marina and Luna streets. It later served as a post office, a public health clinic, and the city hall. Now it serves as a government reception center. See photo at site: www.ponceweb.org/antiguo_casino. html.

sees evidence of eye destruction or deformity. Some of the mountain people keep guinea fowl, but the birds do not usually seem to be in good condition. By the route we travelled today, we drove 84 miles. I was interested by seeing in Ponce the way the Porto Ricans carry their sick to the hospital—two men carry on their shoulders a bamboo pole from which is suspended a hammock shaped like a cigar and completely closed. In this the patients are suspended in comfort completely covered and protected from the eyes of the curious.

Wednesday,
November 9, 1927.

Ponce

On awaking we found that our hosts of the night before, with characteristic Spanish courtesy, had paid all our hotel expenses. We had breakfast at 7 A.M. in the patio—cool and very pleasant—and we then started on the return to San Juan via Salinas, Guayama, Patillas, Yabucoa, Humacao, Gurabo, and Caguas, a drive of 114 miles. As far as Patillas, we drove through coconut plantations and villages along the coast. This part reminded me of Samoa though the villages are not as picturesque. Leaving Maunabo we began to go into the mountains and from the car we had a fine view of the valley and southern sea coast. We passed a giant boulder of about 40 tons which had fallen on the road in a landslide. Humacao is in a valley by the east coast and for some hours or so we coasted along a high cliff above the valley before reaching the town which has a fine church and plaza. Soon after leaving Humacao we called on Mrs. Waller, the wife of the owner of

RAL and Gary Burke at breakfast in the patio of the Hotel Meliá in
Ponce, at 7:00 AM (Photo and comment: F.W. O'Connor)
(Courtesy of the Malloch Rare Book Room of the New York Academy of Medicine Library)

the local and other Centrals—a picturesque and comfortable
house with a spacious sun parlor.

Gurabo is situated well inland and is about 600 feet
above sea level. There are many cases of elephantiasis here.
Today saw several small flamboyant trees in bloom. All along
the Porto Rican roads we see laborers reconstructing and

repairing roads. The stones for the work are still broken by the old primitive method of hand and hammer labor. Several heavy showers of rain today. Back at Condado Vanderbilt at 1 P.M. This morning I carried the bouquet I received last night nearly as far as Santa Isabel till the sun was strong enough when I took the photograph of it. The rest of the day in the hotel reading and writing.

Thursday,
November 10, 1927.

Very wet all day. 8:45 A.M. to Presbyterian Hospital where G. Burke and A. Serra showed me many cases of elephantiasis and the sprue case for which I had recommended treatment and which are progressing well. Then to Tropical School, where I prepared cultures for my mosquito experiments. Back to the hotel, rather tired. Spent the afternoon painting a sea view from the corner room of the northeastern aspect of the hotel, third floor. R.A.L. called with photographs, etc. After dinner, to Amalio Roldán lecture on treatment of G.U.[107] At 11 P.M. Burke, Serra, W.A.H., and I to Presbyterian Hospital, where in 35 minutes we examined 25 bloods for microfilaria before landing a good positive—a woman from whom Burke took about 20 cc of blood from which I inoculated the cultures I had prepared this morning. A nice piece of team work. Over 30 cases examined and blood taken—all done in three quarters of an hour—and I was back in my hotel 55 minutes after entering the hospital. Worked at hotel till 1 A.M. on my discourse for the class tomorrow morning.

---

107   Abbreviation to denote genitourinary infections.

Friday,
November 11, 1927,
Armistice Day.

At Tropical School 8 A.M.—lectured to class on the Four Principal Filariae of man. Then, with R.A.L., to the Military Hospital[108] at San Sebastián [street], where we were met and shown round by Major Wetherall, in command. An old Spanish building erected 100 years ago by the Spanish Archbishop and used from the start as a military hospital. Bad yellow fever epidemics here in the past. Now, Wetherall is initiating improvements. No clinical laboratory till recently. A fine patio in the middle of the building. Wetherall and Captain Blackwell both escorted us and then we drove to Blackwell's house nearby and from his verandah had a glorious view of the bay of San Juan.

We drove to El Castillo del Morro, the fortress built in 1539 which withstood the attacks of Drake in 1595 and fought the Earl of Cumberland, the French and the Dutch at different periods. We walked all over its old battlements, and closer to the sea, guarding the strait, saw the modern gun of which the following tale: This gun guarded the harbour during the world war. An interred German ship tried to get out and the gun fired a shot across its bows, whereat the ship returned to its moorings. It might not have done so had its officers known that with the discharge of the shell the gun burst its moorings and ran about the battlement. Officers' quarters in another old

---

108 Located in Old San Juan, it was established for the city poor by Bishop Fray Manuel Jiménez Pérez, but when construction ended in 1782, it was converted into a military hospital. After the 1898 American occupation, it was maintained as a military hospital. Today it houses a government sponsored School of Plastic Arts.

Castle of El Morro surmounting heights above strait - In foreground, the refuse heaps and shacks of La Perla
(Photo and comment: F.W. O'Connor)
(Courtesy of the Malloch Rare Book Room of the New York Academy of Medicine Library)

building near El Morro are not as good and the officers make much complaint.

After this visit, Blackwell left us and R.A.L. and I drove down to the sea shore to that last resort of degraded humanity—La Perla.[109] It is outside the city limits and beyond the control of the Public Health Department, and combined in a confusion of filth one sees the Red Light Area, resort of criminals, and a hospital, or rather a refuge where the indigent sick, largely venereal or tubercular, congregate to end their vile existences. There is no sanitation anywhere and sewage and refuse pour down the sides of the cliffs from the houses to pass by gutters past the buildings on the sea front. No one dare land here and all the improvident can build their overcrowded shacks and crude sheds where every sanitary law is broken. The visit brought to mind Dickens's[110] description of London squalor in the early nineteenth century. It is hard to realize that such a condition can exist in our days and immediately

109   An urban slum in Old San Juan, on a steep slope outside of the old city walls facing the Atlantic Ocean.
110   Charles Dickens (1812-1870).

adjacent to such good evidence of progress. I saw a severe case of Granuloma inguinale[111] here. The sick were in the worst state of filth on cots with dirty linen and the look on most faces was one of despair. The most revolting states of illness were to be seen here. A Dr. Rodriquez[112] has now taken charge and this nice young fellow is endeavoring to institute changes. Before his coming last week there was no one to look after the poor brutes. The sick are the waifs and strays from all parts of the Island who have no friends or relatives and who on account of the vileness of their conditions cannot get care anywhere else.

To School and then to hotel. Lunch. Painting till 3:45. Then to School, where Ortiz gave an admirable lecture on Rural Sanitation and Hookworm.

[Notes from Ortiz lecture]

Hookworm:
Campaign work. July 1, 1921–June 30, 1927

Census	Infected	Treated	Total Treated	Cured
335,433	287,170	278,643	776,505 [?]	233,052

Infection 80% [86%?]. Cures 84%. Total latrines constructed to date (in 6 years) 107,118.

$500,000 spent in 20 years. Survey after 20 years' routine dispensary work showed 90% infection.

---

111   An uncommon disease transmitted through direct contact with lesions during sexual activity. It produces slowly spreading painless ulceration of the genitalia and anal region and is attributed to Calymmatobacterium granulomatis. See: http://www.nlm.nih.gov/medlineplus/ency/article/000636.htm.

112   R. Rodríguez Molina.

The year 1926-1927. Representing one year's work:

Census	Infected	Treated	Total Treated	Cured
86,029	57,625	72,363 [?]	138,779 [?]	61,301 [?]

Latrines constructed 20,792 and reinspection work on old existing latrines.
Department of Health
Commissioner of Health
Assistant Commissioner of Health
Board of Health [/] Legislature [?]

1. Chemical Labs
2. Bureau of Property & Accts.
3. Biology Lab. (Public Health)
4. Bureau of Vital Statistics
5. Bureau of Sanitary Engineering
6. Bureau of Transmissible Diseases
7. Bureau of General Inspection
8. Public Health Units (and, according to local necessities)
9. Bureau of Rural Sanitation, Hookworm, Malaria, etc.

Giving the people shoes wasted [?] $500,000 in Porto Rico.

Hookworm:
Sanitary Work   Hookworm Company
    Construction   Sanitation
    Use   Treatment
    Conservation   Reinspection
                                        (permanent)

<u>Bureau of Rural Sanitation</u>:

    Chief of the Bureau

    3 Medical Inspectors

    3 General Inspectors (not physicians) each under 1 Medical Inspector

    81 inspectors distributed into 10 zones with 11 inspectors in each. Each zone has about 10 inspectors including the chief. <u>No treatment is begun in any zone until the whole community has constructed latrines</u>. Then, treatment is given to the whole community. The larvae live in the soil for 6 weeks. Parasites live about 6 years in the intestine.

    1st Treatment—Oil of Chenopodium & Carbon Tetrachloride 2-1 [ratio 2:1]

    2nd Treatment—Thymol

    <u>Good Stories</u>. One family built a good latrine, added an annex and moved to the latrine to live. Another family used the latrine for keeping fighting cocks.

    Reinspection is rigid. Soil pollution after latrine construction is penalized. Regular examination of soil for pollution and of latrines with flashlights.

    [End of notes from Ortiz lecture]

    Back to hotel to dress. At 7:10, to Capt. Blackwell's to a big dinner party. Sat next to Mrs. Estes, the Commandant's wife. On my right, a rather charming French woman (Mrs. Simpson). At 9 P.M., we all drove to El Fuerte de San Cristóbal, constructed in 1631,[113] and one of the strongest forts

---

113 In 1634, a small redoubt is built on the high ground known as San Cristóbal on the northeast side of San Juan. 1765-1783—main period of construction of Fort San Cristóbal as we see it today under the directions of Royal Engineers Tomás O'Daly and Juan Mestre. (National Park Service USA)

in Spain's former New World Empire. Here on the roof of the battlements, on cement flooring, with sky above and in bright moonlight, the Armistice Night Ball was held and I enjoyed some very pleasant dances. Between dances walked with partners on the battlements and looked at the sea below, and at one place saw the Haunted Sentry Box,[114] planted on a rocky promontory. Legend has it that the Evil One was wont to abstract the sentries, but the truth probably was that the sentries jumped into the sea to avoid their durance vile and swam ashore, deserting to the interior. There was an excellent Porto Rican band at the dance, conducted by a German band master. Major Wetherall was especially courteous, introducing me to several partners and showing me round the fortress.

Saturday,
November 12, 1927.

Rather tired, but still going strong. W.A.H. calls at 8:15 to show me breeding places of *culicoides*[115] in a brackish swamp by the Condado Lagoon near the hotel. Then, to the School, where I dissected an elephantoid leg and chose tissues for embedding. A strange Dr. Birdwell called and gave me his "opinion on filariasis." Lays great stock on the inguinal glands and inguinal adenitis in cases of filariasis. R.A.L. showed me sections of filarial tissue and schistosomal tissue. Then, we drove to the University of Porto Rico to attend the Faculty luncheon. I sat with Doermann, the Vice Chancellor. One

---

114   Devil's Sentry Box, at the base of a steep cliff, is today the oldest surviving element of San Cristóbal. (National Park Service USA)

115   A type of biting midge which can carry a range of tropical diseases. See: http://www.iah.bbsrc.ac.uk/schools/factfiles/carriers.htm.

of the professors gave a discourse on the Philippines. Later Ortiz called for me and drove me to the Leprosarium near Río Piedras. It is a thoroughly up-to-date institution in a fine open and rich locality in a big plain surrounded on all sides by good views of hills and mountains. All the ground in the compound is tilled by the lepers. The houses are white and of Spanish architecture and look very picturesque. They are arranged in two rows—one for males and the other for females—separated by a broad plantation 200 yards in breadth, and between these rows on a hill is the Administration and Laboratory building. There are 60 patients in the institution, which is full to capacity but the institution does not take all the lepers. There are 4 occupants to each house and each has a separate room with ample ventilation and good lighting. There are bathrooms and cupboards for clothes in each house. In front of each there is a well covered verandah and the whole is surrounded by an ample garden plot which the patients are encouraged to plant and maintain. The lepers lead more or less isolated lives because they not only do not want to be seen by the outside world, but they do not like to be seen by each other. Often they do not get on well together. A few congregate together as plotters against the Administration, or anything, and they sit behind one of the houses and scheme. While leprosy often sterilizes the males it sometimes has the opposite effect with the women, who are the most frequent offenders in the matter of moral turpitude; if discovered they are brazenly candid and refuse to make promises toward amendment. On the whole, the lepers are well behaved, although a few are truculent and I saw one boy of 12 years who was a veritable devil and uncontrollable. The *Fascies leonis*[116] is very common

---

116   Facial deformities observed in advanced cases of leprosy.

View of the Leprosarium of Porto Rico: Two houses - 4 patients in each (Photo and comment: F.W. O'Connor)
(Courtesy of the Malloch Rare Book Room of the New York Academy of Medicine Library)

and every kind of leprosy, tubercular or anesthetic, may be seen. Most are mixed. One case is especially interesting and has never shown dermal signs; has complete muscular atrophy, the lower jaw has fallen from the upper and has to be supported by a rubber band around the head. The muscles of all the limbs are wasted and he walks with a curious shuffling gait. Diagnosis was made when he found a nail had run through his foot from sole to dorsum without his feeling it: a smear from the nose then revealed the leprosy bacillus. Lepers cannot be used in the laundry or cook houses on account of the danger of their being burnt. The youngest leper Ortiz knows was aged 6. Here, there is one of 8 and several between that age and 16. The children of leprous parents are not leprous and may be saved if immediately removed from the parents. The treatment used is with the new Ethyl Ethers of Chaulmoogra Oil,[117] but Ortiz says it is overrated as to value. The patients receive the Ethers twice weekly, 1 minim[118] in saline

---

117 For the use of this product in the treatment of leprosy see: http://lhncbc.nlm.nih.gov/lhc/docs/published/2003/pub2003048.pdf.

118 A minim is a volume measure used by apothecaries equivalent to 1/60 fluidram or .003612 cubic inches.

for adults, then ¼ gram, ½ gram, and after that 3 grams always intravenously. Up to date four lepers have been discharged under supervision. On admission to the leprosarium all patients have to have intestinal parasites removed, and their health improved on general lines, and they get the best of food. Many cases go steadily from bad to worse despite treatment and good care. The staff for the institution is 1 superintendent, 1 male nurse and 2 female nurses. Lepers of opposite sexes, despite their revolting appearance, often become infatuated with each other, and write each other love letters as foolish as those of other mortals. There is admirable opportunity for research here and Ortiz says that the splendid laboratory facilities which he showed me will be at the disposal of anyone who wishes to come here to work and that equipment as well as living quarters and food will be provided for anyone who would be willing to come. The lepers will give every cooperation, as they are always inclined to do with their distressing condition. After the inspection we went to the staff room, and as it was very hot we enjoyed large draughts of a fruit cup composed of fresh pineapple, oranges, and grapefruit. On the way home, we drove through the tuberculosis sanatorium. R.A.L. called for me at Condado Vanderbilt and we went to dine with Dr. and Mrs. Charles Weiss. We left early and went to the Tropical School to collect books for my work tonight, and then back to the hotel where I worked till late.

Sunday,
November 13, 1927.

Awoke several times during the night and this morning with severe pleurodynia[119] which makes it painful and difficult to

---

119   Paroxysmal pain in the intercostals muscles. (*Dorland's Pocket*; op. cit.: 547.)

take a deep breath—pain over spleen—otherwise feeling well and full of beans.[120] Breakfast in my room and worked till 10:45. When R.A.L. arrived we picked up Weiss and drove east along the north shore to the promontory Boca de Cangrejos where Ortiz and about 20 of his friends gathered to give me a *lechón asado* (roast pig), Spanish custom of cooking suckling pigs with lots of other food and ample liquid to wash it down with. Everything was carefully prepared in advance, tables, benches, tents in case of rain, and so on, on this little spit of land with beautiful scenery around us, and a very pleasant lot of fellows, we gave ourselves up to feasting and merriment. The pig meat was good, as also the chicken, and after we had finished we took photographs and watched little nigger[121] babies bathing in the water, while further out we saw the fins of patrolling sharks, looking out for prey. We had lovely weather and altogether thoroughly enjoyed ourselves—some of the guests perhaps too well. We got back to San Juan at 4 P.M. and, after a rest, I spent the remainder of the day at work on the subject of discourse to the parasitology class on the morrow.

Monday,
November 14, 1927.
7:40 A.M. to the Tropical School, where I lectured to

---

120   Full of energy.

121   From the perspective of dominant-racist ideologies, this term was the standard descriptive one used for people of African descent. In British colonial usage, the term was sometimes applied generically to dark-skinned persons of any origin. In O'Connor's day and culture it was used freely. At present, however, it is considered so offensively racist that publications frequently refer to "the n-word" instead of repeating the actual word. For a broader discussion of the word and its usage, see Kennedy, Randal. *Nigger: The Strange Career of a Troublesome Word.* NY: Pantheon Books, 2002.

Hoffman's class on *Dracunculus medinensis*[122] and *Onchocerca volvulus*,[123] (*O. caecutiens*). Then, with R.A.L., to the city about my return passage where I encountered the following red tape:

I. Visit to the emigration department to announce my cause and ask for a sailing permit. Was presented with forms appertaining to same.

II. With forms to the shipping company (Porto Rican Line).[124] Gave them details, and they gave me a slip to take to the doctor on the ship.

III. To ship "S.S. Coamo"[125] examination by doctor—a farce. He signed the paper.

IV. With paper, back to steamship company. Got ticket on payment.

V. Back to emigration department and got permit signed, stamped and sealed—and now I can sail. Then, back to the School, where I saw two very interesting cases of filariasis noted elsewhere.

---

122 A roundworm transmitted through the ingestion of contaminated water, produces inflammation of the skin and deeper tissues. This disease does not occur in Puerto Rico.

123 A filarial worm transmitted by the bite of infected flies, produces onchocerciasis (river blindness). This disease does not occur in Puerto Rico.

124 In the period of O'Connor's Diary, the New York & Porto Rico Line carried passengers and transported perishable and other cargo between the United States and the islands of the West Indies, by oil burning steamers ships, two of which were the S.S. "Borinquen" and the S.S. "Coamo." See: http://www.timetableimages.com/maritime/images,porto34i2.htm.

125 The "S.S. Coamo" was built by the Newport News Shipyard, Newport, Virginia, in 1925. It was torpedoed in 1942 by a German submarine. (Fortunecity.com) See photo at site: http://www.rootsweb.com/~prhgs/photo_25.htm.

Spent the afternoon in my hotel room, preparing my lecture on amebiasis.[126] I had as guests for lunch today, Drs. G. Burke, Cook, W.A.H., Serra and Weiss.

Received a bulky and pleasing mail from New York. Early dinner and then, off to the School, where despite the bad weather a goodly number of physicians, including some from distant towns, came for the lecture which this time was on amebiasis. Some professional photographs were taken in the hall of Ortiz, R.A.L., and me, in one of them with the audience. After the lecture, I examined some hydrocele fluids—all negative. Today Ortiz gave me a splendid collection of photographs, etc. dealing with the activities under his control. He has been extraordinarily kind and cooperative and he has a good show and is rightly proud of it. The Burkes drove me back to the Condado Vanderbilt.

Tuesday,
November 15, 1927.

Aguadilla.

I was up, dressed and ready when G. Burke called at 5:30 A.M. It was raining as we drove in his Essex to his house in the dark. Dr. Alice Burke gave us a good breakfast, and still in the dark we took the road at 6 A.M. It was still drizzling, but as we approached Bayamón the dawn came and the sky cleared and by and by the sun came out. The roads were deserted and we made excellent time, passing through Arecibo at 8 A.M. After this everything was new to me, and I

126 Infection with or disease caused by amebas (a protozoan), especially Entamoeba histolytica. (*Medline Plus Medical Dictionary*)

Burke's "Flyer." An Essex with O'C. during stop for luncheon after leaving Aguadilla
(Photo and comment: F.W. O'Connor)
(Courtesy of the Malloch Rare Book Room of the New York Academy of Medicine Library)

enjoyed the picturesque town of Hatillo, with its pretty church, and Camuy on the coast. Near the coast, in these parts, you see the only thoroughbred and real coconuts. Everywhere else they are standardized as regards size (which is stunted) and nut producing power whereby the owners make money and the country loses much of its beauty. The coast here looks somewhat like the coast in the South Seas. The country is all level or slightly undulating till we reached Quebradillas, after which we came out on a hillside overlooking a gorgeous vista of cliffs with breaking surf and bay at Northwest corner of the Island. Descending to the plain, we turned south and entered a canyon wherein laborers were breaking stones with hand hammers. After we passed through the small town of Isabela— the only endemic area of yaws[127] left on the Island (this being allowed to continue under supervision for comparison and

---

127 An infectious disease that is caused by a spirochete (Treponema pertenue) and that is characterized by a primary ulcerating lesion of the skin followed by a secondary stage in which ulcers develop all over the body and by a third stage in which the bones are involved. (*Medline Plus Medical Dictionary*)

teaching purposes).[128] Finally, on rounding a curve, we came out on a high cliff from which one had a grand view of the west coast of the Island, including the broad semicircular bay in the center of which at the foot of the cliffs is the town of Aguadilla. We drove down the incline to the town which we entered at 9:30 A.M. Having thus completed the 84 miles in 3 ½ hours. Arriving at the Presbyterian Church we found that although 10:30 A.M. was the appointed hour that many patients had already turned up—all the arrangements having been made by Dr. Enrique Koppisch,[129] a native of this town, and G. Burke's interne who had come on the day before to round up cases. His mission proved to be even more fruitful than he had promised. On the church door was a notice in Spanish which read: "On November 14th will come three doctors from the Presbyterian Hospital in San Juan to examine the people with filariasis." Most of the patients were women, as the men doubtless could not leave work. On the basis that men are more frequently infected with filariasis than women, it is probable that there is a very heavy incidence of infection in this town.

We commenced work at 9:45. Burke took patients in one room and I examined patients in another room, with Koppisch giving valuable assistance as interpreter in asking questions. A most interesting and varied assortment of cases.

---

128 Treatment for yaws now consists of a single injection of penicillin. O'Connor is mistaken regarding the use of Isabela as a site for medical education on yaws: see essay in this book by Rigau-Pérez, José G. "The apogee of tropical medicine: An epidemiologic portrait of Puerto Rico in 1927", section on "Diseases transmitted form person to person."

129 Enrique Koppisch, MD (Philadelphia, 1927), later Professor of Pathology at the School of Tropical Medicine.

We examined 50 patients before 1:45 P.M., when we ceased work and during this time Burke tapped four hydroceles. There remained 20 cases which owing to lack of time we could not examine. It was a fine piece of team work and the interest of the cases more than repaid the trouble taken. The town would be well worth an exhaustive survey for filariasis. At 2 P.M. we began the return flight to San Juan, soaring out the town, we stopped a few minutes to get gasoline and then went into the country some distance before stopping again to eat the splendid lunch that Dr. Alice Burke had provided for us— delicious chicken salad, cheese, and coffee. When we ate we realized that we had been famished, but the enthusiasm in the work had made us forget till now. Then on at great speed, but with Burke one felt very safe, his eye being always on the job. It was delightful drive back with the sun shining all the way, and with roads very clear of traffic. We arrived at Cook's house in San Juan at 5:55, got the keys of the School, and drove there to examine the hydroceles, finding all negative. Then, to Condado Vanderbilt Hotel, and I had changed my clothes and was ready again when R.A.L. and Burke arrived at 7 P.M. and drove me to the tuberculosis sanatorium where Ortiz, Fernós and two officers of the sanatorium met us and entertained us. After some refreshing cocktails, we had an excellent dinner with champagne accompaniment. Afterwards, in the cool of the night, we took a walk in the grounds and watched the large bullfrogs in the drive. Fernós, whose parents were Catalonians, told me of the Spanish descendants of the northern Earls, the O'Donnells and O'Neills, O'Dalys, etc., some of whom are now in Porto Rico. In Spanish history these families have been all known as politicians and as generals in the army. Ortiz calls Aguadilla the Chinatown of Porto Rico—very poor, and with the worst sanitation in the Island. Now that sanitation and treatment of hookworm is completed and maintenance is in operation, things may improve in the town. Back to the hotel by 10:15 after having driven today more than 200 miles. Am feeling in fine form after this, the star day of the trip.

Wednesday,
November 16, 1927.

Indigestion during the night and broken sleep. To School at 9 A.M. Cook drove me down and I attended his lecture on the chemical composition of the body—a good lecture, clear and concise. Then some hours with R.A.L. getting some data on local medical and university matters. Lunch at the School. Examined some more hydrocele fluids, both negative. Perhaps periodicity of the parasites in the blood may affect their absence in the fluid during the day. In the afternoon to the Presbyterian Hospital where I saw some cases of sprue and one very typical case. Then to call on Mrs. and Gloria María Ashford.[130] Back to hotel dressed before dinner. To the School with R.A.L. at 8:30. P.D. Ortiz showed an excellent leprosy film—just the kind of thing for propaganda work—and following this, I gave my last lecture, a popular one on Polynesia. About 150 people present, including Colonel Estes, the Commandant. Back to the hotel and packed.

Thursday,
November 17, 1927.

I finished packing and with R.A.L. at 9:30 went to call on the Governor, H. M. Towner, but he was not in and I did

---

130   Wife and daughter of Dr. Bailey K. Ashford, who was not in Puerto Rico at the time.

not see him. We inspected the old gate and the old Spanish wall of San Juan and passed the Cathedral where the bones of Ponce de León[131] have recently been laid, Ashford having been the pall-bearer at the transfer.[132] Then, to the Quarantine Station[133]—met by the Chief of the Bureau of Transmissible Diseases, Dr. Martín O. de la Rosa,[134] who showed us over his bungalow hospital of about forty five beds in which he takes pride. This hospital takes contagious diseases from all over the Island. Saw three more cases of leprosy—a mother and her girl child of six. The latter did not appear to be more than four. No symptoms but nasal smear positive, and that case in a girl aet. 15, looking 10. Both these cases showed retarded development, but the last case has menstruated. Saw another good case of Granuloma inguinale with excellent progress following tartar emetic treatment. Also a case of yaws—the first I have seen in Porto Rico—the yaws being on

---

131   Juan Ponce de León (ca. 1460-1521), Spanish conquistador, was the first Governor of Puerto Rico (1508-1511) by appointment of the Spanish Crown. European discoverer of Florida, in 1513.

132   Ponce de León's remains were transferred from San José Church to the Cathedral of San Juan.

133   Quarantine Hospital, was one of the clinical facilities for the isolation of contagious patients ("for miscellaneous infectious diseases, 30 beds; distance from School by automobile, 5 minutes") used by the School of Tropical Medicine for clinical instruction, during O'Connor's visit. "Announcement 1926-1927." Archivo Central UPR.

134   Martín O. de la Rosa, MD (Seville), was listed as part of the faculty at the School of Tropical Medicine as Assistant Professor of Communicable Diseases (Faculty, 1927-28).Together with Dr. Eduardo Garrido Morales, he offered "lectures and demonstrations" on "Tropical Epidemiology" at the School. "Announcement 1926-1927." Archivo Central UPR.

the abdomen. Then, Dr. Eduardo Garrido Morales,[135] whose office is in the same compound, explained his organization of epidemiological studies, showing how information was collected and gave me sample cards indicating the whole process which seems to be working well. Many diseases are notifiable that are not so elsewhere, e.g., filariasis, sprue, helminthiasis.[136]

To Condado Vanderbilt Hotel where the following lunched with me: R.A.L, Ortiz, Fernós, Martínez, Carrión, and Ferrer. After luncheon goodbyes, and R.A.L. drove me to School where I said goodbye to the staff after lunch. Then, to S.S. "Coamo." Goodbye to Jenaro and R.A.L. After boarding the ship Drs. Carrión and Martínez came to the dock, but I could not get off to speak to them. The boat sailed in the rain, half an hour late, at 3:30 P.M. Before leaving, R.A.L. gave me Lafcadio Hearn's "Two Years in the French West Indies."[137]

Gist of talk with Lambert about Tropical School and University matters

The School

The one routine service of the School for the outside is the laboratory service in pathology, because pathology is not provided for on the Island. Routine stool examinations and Wassermanns are not done.

---

135   Eduardo Garrido Morales, MD (1924, Med. Col. Virginia) and Dr. Public Health (1926, Johns Hopkins). Epidemiologist with the Puerto Rico Department of Health (1926-1933), who became Commissioner of Health in 1933. He was listed as part of the faculty of the School of Tropical Medicine as Instructor in Epidemiology. "School of Tropical Medicine, Faculty, 1927-28." Archivo Central UPR.
136   An infection with worms.
137   First published in 1890, offers a detailed account of day to day life in the Caribbean.

110 out of 300 active physicians of the Island have used the laboratory. Up to date 1,146 miscellaneous specimens (mostly surgical) have been examined and reported on.

91 autopsies have been done during the last 19 months. The number could be moderately increased by taking material from the tuberculosis sanatorium but a further increase at the present time would imperil the thoroughness of the work. About 25 blocks are made and cut from each autopsy.

The work could be enormously extended if desirable (for instance at La Perla where all bodies are unclaimed). The best material comes from the Presbyterian Hospital—a 75 bed hospital—where they get 75% of the autopsies.

R.A.L. is opposed to duplicating the work of the Health Department by doing water analysis, etc. Clinical-pathological conferences are held every two weeks.

Budgets

1926   Regular Appropriation Government, University of Porto Rico, $30,500

       as for the old Institute: $15,000

       Columbia gives:

                                     $45,000

       Spent: $50,000

       Deficit made up by the University of Porto Rico

1927   Govt. of Porto Rico University: $30,500

       Columbia (roughly): $20,000

       Available money for year: $50,500

              Expected expenditure: $56,000

              Expected deficit $5,500

R.A.L. expects to meet deficit by tuition fees of this and last year and any extra amount available from the University.

The Columbia money is spent directly in payment of salaries of four American personnel and visiting lecturers.

The University appropriation is paid in other salaries and for maintenance.

Honorary lecturers and Presbyterian Hospital personnel get no salary from the School.

The budget to be nearly safe should be $75,000. Present conditions meet only an Assistant Professor of Parasitology and a part-time Bacteriologist.

The Hospital for Tropical Disease[138] adjacent to the School should be completed next summer. It will contain 45 beds. Money for this institution is appropriated for a district hospital under the Department of Health. Clinicians will be appointees of the School in conference with the Department of Health.

<u>The University</u>

Finances from Insular Government 2 million tax and special funds from other taxes. Annual revenue $700,000 must take care of new buildings as well as maintenance. Now spending $200,000 in buildings in present stage of transition.

Includes: 1. Plant at Río Piedras
2. Plant of Agriculture and Engineering, Mayagüez
3. Tropical School $30,500

Chancellor Benner feels that the Tropical School should not be a burden on the University. University has 1,000 students exclusive of High School and Practical School; 200 of the 1,000 are in the Agricultural School.

---

138   This structure, located in the west side of the School of Tropical Medicine became a student's dormitory when the institution was converted to the School of Medicine of the University of Puerto Rico. Subsequently it was vacated and a School of Dentistry was established in the same facilities.

Faculties

Law, Liberal Arts, including Biology, Pharmacy, Agriculture, Engineering, School of Business, Tropical Medicine. Master's degree only in Spanish and Education, but this year also in Biology. Biology to be partly done at the Tropical School which will give credits.

Columbia and the agreement

Columbia agrees only to be responsible for the salary of the Director of the School of Tropical Medicine, but since has informally agreed to pay the salaries of two more professors and this year will cover the salaries of three as well as the Director, one being part-time and leaving a balance for visiting lecturers. But nothing is binding beyond the Director's salary. Most of the money from Columbia is from DeLamar Fund.[139]

Tuition last year brought $1,900. This fund is used for special needs, special technical equipment, etc.

Tropical School

Last year, 29 students, of which 22 physicians, 7 B.A.s. This year, 14 physicians, 8 B.A.s. Money for future is not certain. Ashford gets no salary.

Weather fine but a heavy swell. My cabin 109, with the same steward as on the downward trip. Received invitation to dine at Captain's table.

---

139   Joseph R. DeLamar (1842-1918), a Dutch born sea captain who became a successful mine owner and Idaho state senator. Upon his death he left a substantial estate to be divided among "the three medical schools of the day—John Hopkins, Harvard and Columbia." These funds contributed to the expansion of the schools during the Depression by supporting numerous teaching and research initiatives. (John Hopkins University website)

Friday,
November 18, 1927.

Fine weather but heavy swell rolling towards U.S. coast from the Atlantic. Ship rolls. Captain tells me this line has been running for 35 years and therefore before the American occupation. Till America took the Island most of the merchandise for Porto Rico came from Spain. This is the first trip that the ship has been "WET," the liquor being shipped at Santo Domingo on the Island of Santo Domingo. At our table all Irish: a North of Ireland keen Presbyterian in the linen trade; Kelly a Catholic sugar planter of Santo Domingo; Harrigan, an Irish Commodore who is in general a rather offensive person. The Presbyterian tells me that there are over 30 competitors in the embroidery business. Read some of Hearn's book—a very interesting and colorful one.

Saturday,
November 19, 1927.

Passed the S.S. "San Lorenzo" delayed one day by storm.

A Mr. Connelly, a pharmacist of Buffalo, amused me immensely by his experience regarding his own ailments with doctors in group practice. Rough sea towards evening and all night. Reading Hearn. Flying fish can still be seen.

Passed Cape Hatteras. Calm. Lots of sargasso in sea. Reading Hearn. Much amused by a passenger now an engineer in the boiler trade. I had noticed him watch the card players in the smoking room with a sleepy but intelligent eye. Presently he told me that he was brought up as a carnival manager, and with the most cold-blooded effrontery he described in detail the methods of robbing the laity who went to carnivals for amusement, and how easy it was to hoodwink the public. But his conscience was too delicate for the trade and he had to give it up, and with the profits he took a course of engineering, and then he said, "But Doctor, what I could never understand is this—that in my game scientists and so-called brainy men are the bigger suckers, and amongst those, doctors are so pathetically easy that after doing one or two I never had the heart to fleece them any more." Incidentally he informed me that he still carried "doctored" dice, and showed me a set explaining that he only used them for the purpose of fleecing a rogue when he found him despoiling others. "It's my way" he ended "of paying back a little of what I took when I was a young and misguided man." A very refreshing rogue.

Monday,
November 21, 1927.
At Quarantine 5 A.M. Alongside 9 A.M. Disembarked 10 A.M. Home at 66 Barrow Street[140] 11 A.M.

Summary of Impressions of Porto Rico Trip
1. An island beautiful, and good roads make all its beauty accessible. A quiet people, handsome in the main, and picturesque, not over curious, kindly and very hospitable, sensitive, excitable, and when quarrelsome unkind especially by word written or spoken—therefore their press is a dangerous organ. Exploited by absentee landlords who leave no chances for the small producer.
2. Appalling poverty, overpopulation, ill nourishment

---

140   There is a "66 Barrow Street" in Greenwich Village, West, Lower Manhattan, NY City, between Bedford and Hudson Streets.

and high incidence of disease, with high mortality and especially high infantile mortality. Much ignorance and superstition. All this makes them a prey to trust monopolies of foreigners.

3. A craze for improvement and learning. The great number of schools well attended is a good sign. The willingness of patients to be examined should encourage doctors. The medical profession's reaction to R.A.L.'s splendid efforts along medical lines is most encouraging. Ortiz a great force, and marvelous advances are being made under his administration. It is a matter for speculation if such another can be found if he ever goes. Politics, as in all other countries, and especially in Latin countries, is a curse here.

Many tropical diseases are present on the Island—malaria, sprue, dengue, hookworm, schistosomiasis (Mansoni), ascaris, pellagra, leprosy, and filariasis are all very prevalent. The dysenteries, yaws, and numerous skin diseases also occur, and there are probably other conditions, for the Island has not been surveyed. There are diseases of domestic animals, especially Texas fever of the cattle requiring consideration, and there is an extensive field in entomology to be investigated from all points. The splendid preventive work administered by the Department of Health and the antimalaria work of the Rockefeller Foundation create visions in the mind of a splendid training center in hygiene. To sum up, the diseases are present in plenty, and with the enthusiasm and cooperation of the Commissioner of Health and his officers, the Director of the School of Tropical Medicine and his staff, and the staffs of the Presbyterian and Municipal hospitals, and the willingness of the people to be examined, there are all the facilities for medical research under very ideal conditions. One feels that before long Porto Rico should make valuable contributions to medicine.

2

Francis William O'Connor:
An Irishman Who Loved
the Tropics

Annette B. Ramírez de Arellano

Francis W. O'Connor's life began during Queen Victoria's reign and ended during Franklin Delano Roosevelt's New Deal. Although he lived only 54 years, his life played out over several continents and covered an unusually rich period in the history of medicine. It spanned the bacteriological revolution, the establishment of tropical medicine as an academic discipline, and the transformation of medical education. These events, together with World War I, shaped much of O'Connor's life and career.[1]

---

1   Among O'Connor's papers there is a hand-written notebook titled "A Brief Account of My Life." This was penned in 1922 and is addressed to his children, from whom he was estranged. This narrative covers the first 25 years of his life, from his birth to 1909. This account is the source for most of the events of this period described in this essay. Papers of Dr. Francis William O'Connor, Historical Collections, New York Academy of Medicine, New York, New York (This source is hereafter referred to as "A Brief Account of My Life," NYAM; the pages are not numbered, so it is not possible to provide a more exact reference).

O'Connor was born on May 13, 1884, in County Limerick, Ireland, a country of which it has been said that "the inevitable never happens and the unexpected constantly occurs."[2] He was the fourth child of a "pure Celtic family of the clan O'Connor... of Offaly."[3] There was nothing exciting in the history of his ancestors, who were, for the most part, country gentry living in Tipperary or Limerick. Staunch adherents of the Catholic Church, they kept the faith even during "penal times," when the English Protestant parliament passed a series of anti-Catholic laws intended to maintain the supremacy of the Protestant ascendancy while containing and neutralizing the Irish Catholics. However monolithic in their faith, the O'Connors were more eclectic politically; various family members served with distinction in English armies while others served on the Irish or 'liberating' side.

An Irish Childhood

O'Connor's father, after whom he was named, was a distinguished surgeon with an extensive consulting practice and a Senior Consulting Surgeon at Barrington Hospital. The mother, Ellen O'Carroll O'Connor, had an active role in the community, taking part in many charities and local celebrations. They kept a busy household of five children, two girls and three boys. Francis described his home as a "jolly house" until the time he was six, when his father died unexpectedly of pneumonia, contracted while caring for their sick maid.

---

2   Quote from Sir John Pentland Mahaffy, in Stanford, W.B. and McDowell, R.B., *Mahaffy* (1971), cited in Tony Augarde, ed. *Oxford Dictionary of Modern Quotations*. Oxford: Oxford University Press, 1991: 145.

3   "A Brief Account of My Life," NYAM.

Altered family circumstances led to further changes, which were particularly wrenching for Mrs. O'Connor. Her husband not being insured, his income died with him. Mrs. O'Connor had to discharge their retinue of servants, sell some property, and move to Dublin.

For Francis, the move to Dublin and the new environment were not unwelcome. They took a big house with a fine garden facing a large field, and he recalled those days as very happy ones. In Dublin, Francis and his younger brother Dick went to a school taught by nuns, but they left suddenly because a nun struck Dick in the face with a cane. They transferred to the St. Mary's Day College for Boys, where Francis learned the first ethical commandment of the public school boy, namely "Never to tell;" i.e., not to tattle on others.[4] This lesson he carried with him to his next school, Clongowes Wood College, a prestigious Jesuit boarding school for boys. There, institutionalized sadism on the part of the faculty combined with bullying on the part of students to keep the latter "in line" and ever fearful of impending threats. Those who did not know their lessons were routinely required to kneel in the middle of the class.[5] Students who ran afoul of the school's expectations and requirements soon found themselves flogged or worse.[6] The prefect Mr. Mahoney, who

---

4   The importance of this lesson was stressed by James Joyce, who would later coincide with O'Connor at Clongowes Wood College. When deposited in boarding school, Joyce's character Stephen Daedalus is warned by his father that he should "never peach on a fellow." *A Portrait of the Artist as a Young Man*. New York: Penguin Books, 1964: 9.

5   Ibid.: 47.

6   Ibid.: 44. The instrument used for harsh punishment was the pandybat, made of whalebone and leather with lead inside. James Joyce describes that, upon finding that one of their classmates had transgressed, the students at Clongowes would chant: "It can't be helped; / It must be done. / So down with your breeches / And out with your bum."

was called "Spanks," once even struck him across the head:

> When I next remember anything…it was several
> days later. I was told by Dick that after "Spanks" had
> struck me I remained motionless on the ground and
> "Spanks" was very frightened. I was carried to the
> infirmary and placed in bed under the care of Kate
> Gannon, an old, good-natured but very ignorant
> woman, for in those days there were no nurses at the
> College. An MO [medical officer] came to see me. It
> was thought that I would die…I lapsed into a semi-
> coma; I lay listlessly in bed, gradually sinking.[7]

Mrs. O'Connor was informed, and she rushed to see Francis. Alarmed at his condition, she insisted that Francis' uncle, an experienced clinician, see him. Uncle Charlie continued to make daily visits until Francis was on the way to recovery, an experience which led the youngster to appreciate the wonderful medical skill which he much later, with mature knowledge of the profession, was able to confirm in his uncle.

After a long convalescence at home, Francis returned to school. In his absence, Kate Gannon had been pensioned and "Spanks" Mahoney was gone. But the latter was replaced by a worse man, Mr. Buny, who "was suspicious, leapt about in soft felt slippers, and was ever in search for evidence of wrongdoing amongst the boys."[8] Francis was the innocent victim of Mr. Buny's severity and proclivities.

Both the school's policies on corporal punishment and its policing of collegial behavior had their counterpart among

---

7   "A Brief Account of My Life," NYAM.
8   Ibid.

the students. Bullies preyed upon impressionable youths. After "Spanks" and Buny, Francis' next "source of sorrows" was a bully by the name of Dick Shiel. Feeling persecuted and living in a state of anxiety in anticipation of pain, Francis finally exploded. One day, when Shiel began bullying him with thongs, Francis "flew in an uncontrollable rage and smacked a blow to his face."[9] Francis had discovered his strength and his power. After that, Shiel left him alone and even became his friend to some extent. With this experience behind him, Francis took up boxing with gloves, indulged more in sports, and in time became physically stronger.

Francis' troubles in school coincided with a turbulent time for the O'Connor family. Monoola, the farm which was supporting the family, became the source of litigation and strife and Mrs. O'Connor had no choice but to sell the farm at a dead loss.[10]

Mrs. O'Connor had to leave Ireland in 1898, although the boys continued to attend school in Ireland. Once, while heading back to Clongowes, where he was so terribly unhappy, Francis ran away, but failing to find suitable employment, he decided to return to Chester to look for work in the Dublin Wharves. At the Chester Station he saw his forlorn mother walking on the platform, searching for him. The sight of his mother's anguish eroded all his previous determination. Bracing himself for a severe scolding, he went up to her and surrendered. He described how much he had suffered at school, and she promised him that this would be his last year

---

9   Ibid.

10   The sale price for the farm of 97 acres was 800 pounds. Ibid.

at Clongowes. Francis' return to Ireland was greeted with wild delight by Dick, and they went back to school for a school year that was less irksome because it was to be their final one.

A Physician-in-Training

In the summer of 1901 Francis and Dick joyfully left Clongowes and moved to England. As the sons and nephews of physicians, they were both on track to enter the medical profession. They were admitted into St. Bartholomew's Hospital and College.[11] Founded in 1123, it was one of the oldest and most distinguished hospitals in the world. Built as a palace for the poor, St. Bart's, as it was commonly referred to, was the intellectual home of many medical notables such as William Harvey, who discovered the circulation of blood, and Elizabeth Blackwell, the first woman doctor in the British Isles.

For Francis and Dick O'Connor, St. Bart's proved to be an inspired choice. In 1901, England was entering the reign of Edward VII and was eager to shed the strictures of Victorian conservatism.[12] Medical education was in the midst of a dramatic metamorphosis designed to incorporate the discoveries of the previous decades. The years after 1880 had ushered in the golden age of bacteriology, and the doctrine of specific etiology now undergirded progressive medical

---

11   For a brief history of the hospital, see: www.bartsandthelondon.org.uk.

12   Among the major pressures for change were trade unionism, party politics, and the feminist movement. It was a time of ideological conflicts, which one author has described as "manifestations of a deep self-questioning at all levels of society, which shadowed the confidence of Britain as still, seemingly, the world's most powerful nation." Thompson, Paul. *The Edwardians: The Remaking of British Society*. Bloomington and London: Indiana University Press, 1975: 5.

thinking; in the words of George Rosen: "As if a dam had burst, causative organisms of various diseases were demonstrated in rapid succession, often several in one year."[13]

New paradigms of disease causation swept aside long-accepted theories, prompting the adoption of new treatments and transforming the teaching and practice of medicine and public health. The sciences received priority in the medical curriculum: in 1885 chemistry and physics were offered before the pre-clinical subjects, and hygiene and mental diseases were added as requirements. A further revision enacted in 1890 lengthened the course of study, adding a full year. While St. Bart's, like all medical colleges in England, sought to produce an "omni-competent general practitioner,"[14] it was also intent on keeping current with new educational trends. Debates concerning the relative importance of bedside medicine vs. science, and skills vs. knowledge, were the order of the day. Traditionally regarded as a conservative institution, St. Bart's was nevertheless at the forefront of change, particularly with regard to curriculum change and the introduction of laboratory science into medical teaching.[15]

The O'Connors were entering medicine at a time when the sphere of prevention was expanding and population-based health seemed purchasable. The years from 1904 to 1914 marked the sanitation of the Panamá Canal Zone, called "one of the great achievements" in the history of preventive

---

13   Rosen, George. *Preventive Medicine in the United States, 1900-1975: Trends and Interpretations*. New York, NY: Science History Publications, 1975: 20.

14   Poynter, F.N.L. "Medical Education in England since 1600." In C.D. O'Malley, ed. *The History of Medical Education*. UCLA Forum in Medical Sciences, No. 12. Los Angeles: University of California Press, 1979; 236: 244-245.

15   Waddington, K. *Medical Education*, op. cit.: 116.

medicine. Yellow fever, which was epidemic in 1905, was quelled within two years. In the Canal Zone, cases of malaria declined 91% between 1906 and 1913.[16] While these events were transpiring an ocean away, they were nevertheless part of the daily headlines as well as the growing medical literature.

Although the O'Connor brothers were "raw young Irishmen with broad brogues, full of life, and very young to start medical school" (Francis was 17 and Dick, only 16), they adapted well to the heady environment of St. Bart's.[17] Indeed, they now entered the six happiest years of both their lives. St. Bart's opened new worlds to them both intellectually and socially. They made lifelong friends, and greatly enjoyed their academic years.

Francis suffered the first serious "laceration of his heart,"[18] falling in love with a Dorothy Harrison. She caused him to lose his appetite and sleep and to develop "a tendency to sighs and a love of poetry: in fact, all the signs accepted by writers as diagnostic of the real affection."[19] This lasted for only six months, he proving to be the fickle party in the couple's eventual break-up. He also made Jewish friends, one of them nurturing Francis' love of literature by carefully selecting books that he would enjoy.

The satisfying years of medical school would nevertheless be punctuated with great loss. In 1905, Aileen, the

---

16   Wilson, Charles Morrow. *Ambassadors in White: The Story of American Tropical Medicine*. New York, NY: Henry Holt, and Co., 1942: 63.

17   According to Paul Thompson, *The Edwardians*, op.cit.: 11, in the early twentieth century, "wealth, birth, and manners constituted the three prime qualifications for commanding obedience and respect from others." The O'Connor brothers lacked wealth, but were apparently well-endowed with the remaining two attributes.

18   "A Brief Account of My Life," NYAM.

19   Ibid.

second of the five O'Connor siblings, developed pneumonia and died at home, leaving a husband and two children. Mrs. O'Connor, who was greatly affected by her daughter's death, became very ill in the fall of 1905, dying in October of that year. With her death, Francis lost not only "the noblest woman [he] ever knew, but also the one who "instilled in [him] those ideals which determined [his] high opinion of her sex."[20]

This loss also led him to seriously question his religious faith. Already a skeptic, he could not reconcile the death of his mother with the existence of a just and merciful God. To Francis, the fact that Ellen O'Connor had died before seeing any of her hopes realized—namely, the marriage of her surviving daughter and the qualification of her sons—was particularly cruel. He therefore rejected most religious dogma, although he learned to believe in a "supreme being or supernatural controlling influence who decided our destiny."[21]

A Clinical Career

After a brief hiatus, Francis and Dick returned to St. Bartholomew's. At the end of 1906 Francis passed his qualifying examinations in Medicine and Midwifery, but failed Surgery, the subject he knew best. In early 1907 Dick passed his exams and joined the Royal Army Medical Corps. Later, Francis finally passed his exams, thus qualifying to practice medicine. He immediately went to Seaman's Hospital in Greenwich, to do a

---

20   Ibid.
21   Ibid.

locum for a colleague.[22] There he met Dr. Lawrence McGavin, a surgeon who was to prove helpful in future years.

At Christmas he went to Ireland, where he assisted his Uncle Charlie in his practice. While there, an outbreak of smallpox occurred, and O'Connor was assigned to deal with it. His base of operations was an isolation unit adjoining the local infirmary, and he assumed responsibility for running it and inoculating the population. He had 14 cases of smallpox as in-patients, which he tended to with the help of a day and a night nurse. After six weeks at the unit, O'Connor received news from McGavin about an opening at Seaman's Hospital. O'Connor applied and was chosen for the position, moving back to Greenwich as the full holder of an appointment. Working once again with McGavin, he continued honing his clinical skills, doing major surgery under the guidance of his mentor.

In 1908 O'Connor would suffer the first of several illnesses that would shape his life. He developed suppurative tonsillitis and was operated on. This was followed by a severe bout of rheumatism. It was the beginning of a crippling illness: soon, he could neither move nor dress without help. His brother Dick became his nurse, helping Francis walk and taking him out for drives. Francis was convinced that the chalky soil of Salisbury was making him worse, so he moved to London with what little money he had. This ushered in a time of both terrible suffering and privations but also great satisfaction:

> ...I was very crippled and with sticks would get as
> far as Hyde Park, where I would lie on the grass

---

22   The system of locum tenens (literally, 'place holder,' in Latin; 'holding the place of another,' 'a substitute') allowed doctors to substitute for each other, covering vacations or otherwise filling in for colleagues who had to absent themselves.

for I could not afford a chair and I liked the green and there I would talk and fraternize with London's lower life beggars, thieves, ex-prisoners, prostitutes, postmen and policemen. I from that learned the wonderful amount of good that is to be found in everyone if one but seeks. Included among the most ostracized I found the greatest degree of human feeling and suffering and misfortune ...The most flagrant harlots on learning of my poverty have asked me to share their lowly repasts. During this period of experiences I learned to take a broader view of people and refrain from condemning on appearances.[23]

Worldly Wanderlust

In the autumn of 1908, still sick and weak, O'Connor came to a crossroads in his life. He did not know what direction his career would take. An acquaintance secured him an appointment as ship's doctor in the Union Castle Company, which plied the seas between England and South Africa, delivering mail and passengers. This not only opened up a new career but also promised a possible cure to his ailments. The prevailing medical opinion was that another winter would kill him, and that perspiring might prove therapeutic. In his words,

> ...the trip to the Tropics combined to give me a chance at improvement and from the small salary I

---

23   Ibid.

was enabled to live. Thus through illness I was to go
abroad and acquire that love of the hot countries and
color which was to give me my future career and in
part (for there were other influences later) ordain that
I should become a nomad and spend much of my
time abroad...[24]

Appointed Medical Officer on the SS Galeka,[25]
O'Connor joined the ship, then lying at Blackwell Dock.
Adapting quickly to his new circumstances, he learned that
steamship lines had two classes of men: the all-powerful office
people and the seamen. The former, whose major concern was
financial, were in control when the ship was in its home port.
But as soon as the anchor was weighed, the seamen came into
their own, quite literally ruling the waves. O'Connor found the
seamen full of good humor, civility, honesty and generosity,
and concluded that the British mercantile services contained
some of the finest men in the country. He spent much of his
time with the officers and seamen, because he found them
more "kindly and instructive"[26] than the passengers.

Steaming down the Thames towards Southampton,
O'Connor began his new life. The Galeka sailed to the Bay of
Biscay, in the direction of Las Palmas in the Canary Islands.
The tropical environment was a revelation:

As we neared Las Palmas, the weather grew warmer
and I began to feel better. The moment we anchored
before Las Palmas I knew that I had found an

---

24   Ibid.

25   This ship was later commandeered for use during World War I, and was destroyed
by mines in 1916. See: http://www.union-castle-line.com/history/1990.htm.

26   "A Brief Account of My Life," NYAM.

atmosphere that suited me: the warmth and sun, the bright colors, the great light and the astounding clarity of the atmosphere exaggerating the beauty of the landscape.[27]

The ship was in the Canaries for only a few hours and then the Galeka sailed through glassy smooth seas for several days, finally anchoring in Lobito Bay, in Portuguese West Africa.[28] The tropics had worked their magic on the young Irishman: "By this time I was a restored man. I had no pain. I was well and full of the joy of living. I partook of all games and amusements and I read much for I had brought many of the classics with me."[29] O'Connor's first experience of Africa was indeed a memorable one.

By the next port of call, Cape Town, O'Connor was fully recovered. He was able to climb the precipitous Table Mountain which dominates the landscape, escaping poisonous snakes in the process. He also toured the city, visiting the home of Cecil Rhodes, the Botanical Gardens, and Lion's Head Mountain. The next stops were ports on the eastern coast of South Africa, after which the ship began its voyage home.

It was winter in England on the Galeka's arrival, and the ship proceeded to the European continent towards Hamburg and Antwerp. The round trip on the Galeka lasted almost six weeks, yet O'Connor found it all too brief. After Antwerp, he requested a change of ship because he wanted to make a more extensive voyage and see more of the world. He was therefore

---

27   Ibid.

28   Portuguese West Africa is now Angola.

29   "A Brief Account of My Life," NYAM.

assigned to the SS Armadale Castle, a bigger ship that was better appointed than its sister vessels.[30]

On the Armadale Castle, O'Connor went to Mauritius, where he found that the tropics held health risks of their own. There were a number of malaria convalescents from Mauritius on board and the young medical officer had himself been bitten by mosquitoes when he had debarked in Port-Louis. On the way home, O'Connor had his first attack of Quartan malaria, with high fever that made him delirious. He then had a fever every 72 hours. Seeing a physician upon arrival in England, O'Connor confirmed that he had the malaria parasite in his blood, and had to give up service with the Union Castle Line for treatment. After a few weeks of convalescence, he was well enough to do a *locum tenens*, and to once again assist his Uncle Charlie in his practice, later doing a *locum* for him while he was away.

The Year of Destiny

The year 1909 turned out to be the "year of destiny" for O'Connor. His ambitions and future career were shaped then. Years later, he would regard that period as a great watershed. Prior to that he was "just a boy full of enthusiasm and the joy of living."[31] In addition to the love and camaraderie of his brother Dick, he had lots of friends and was popular and welcome wherever he went. Although he had undergone a terrible illness, he had not been unhappy: he had taken advantage of the forced leisure to develop an inquiring mind

---

30   See: http://www.red-duster.co.uk/UNION2.htm for a brief history of the Union-Castle Line.

31   "A Brief Account of My Life," NYAM.

and an enduring love for art and literature, which gave him great pleasure.

Now he had the opportunity to further his interest in public health and tropical medicine. In 1909 he was a resident medical officer at the Albert Dock Hospital in London, which was part of the Seaman's Hospital where O'Connor had had an earlier affiliation. There he met Dr. Patrick Manson and established a close relationship with the man who would later be known as "the father of tropical medicine."

A Scotsman by birth, Manson had studied medicine at the University of Aberdeen and made his career in Formosa,[32] China, and Hong Kong, where he lived between 1866 and 1889. In 1877-79 Manson had discovered that the mosquito can host a developing parasite worm that causes the human disease filariasis, a finding that assured him a place in the annals of medicine and gave him the nickname of "Mosquito Manson" among legions of medical students. He also hypothesized that mosquitoes were involved in the transmission of malaria, although he was unable to prove this. In 1889 Manson returned to England, expecting to enter a life of semi-retirement and research. But a financial setback forced him to resume the practice of medicine, and he opened a practice in London, devoting himself primarily to the exotic diseases of tropical countries. He also accepted a position at the Seamen's Hospital.

Over the next decade, the matter of improving the medical service of the British colonies in West Africa gained political currency. The tropics were labeled the "white man's grave," disease being responsible for an unusually high death

---

32   Now called Taiwan.

toll among colonial personnel.[33] A particular concern was that newly-appointed medical officers sent to Africa lacked special training in the diagnosis and treatment of tropical diseases and were therefore ill-equipped to address the health needs of the populations they purported to serve. In 1898 the British Secretary of State for the Colonies entrusted Manson and the Seaman's Hospital with developing the field of tropical medicine as a specific field of knowledge. The hospital readily acceded to the request, and the London School of Tropical Medicine was created as part of the hospital, opening for teaching and research on October 2, 1899.

The founding of the new school marked the launching of the formal discipline of "tropical medicine." Liverpool's School of Tropical Medicine opened approximately 6 months earlier, but only because London's initiative had led Liverpool's merchants to sponsor a 'rival' school.[34] London's prominence as a cosmopolitan center and the capital of the British Empire assured that its school would be the preeminent force in the discipline. By the turn of the century, tropical medicine had all the hallmarks of a scholarly discipline: dedicated institutions and curricula, research activities, publications, and a growing cadre of academicians and practitioners whose expertise was confined to the diseases of a particular ecology, warm climates.

By 1909, Manson was widely recognized as a medical luminary; knighted in 1903, he was one of the founders and

---

33   Williams, P.O. "The Scientific Neglect of Tropical Medicine." In Clive Wood, ed. *Tropical Medicine from Romance to Reality*. London: Academic Press, 1978: 18.

34   While the London school was conceived first, its long gestation had allowed Liverpool to get a head start in developing its own school.

the first president of the Royal Society of Tropical Medicine in 1907.[35] O'Connor was full of devotion and admiration for the noted scientist and physician. At the same time, Manson recognized in O'Connor the "perfervidness which goes to make a good clinical investigator."[36] Although Manson was 40 years older than O'Connor, the two men developed an easy, collegial relationship. Manson, who exuded charm and radiated conviviality,[37] teased his younger colleague by stating that the Irish were a "bad lot."[38] When O'Connor, always a proud Celt, protested, Manson countered that O'Connor had been saved from his countrymen's fate only because "we caught you young and more or less civilized you."[39] Still, O'Connor felt that Manson, though a most patriotic Scot, "loved Ireland and the Irish and moreover understood them."[40] With his "keen sense of humor," Manson occasionally called his young

---

35   For biographies of Sir Patrick Manson, see Manson-Bahr, P. and Alcock, A. *Life and Work of Sir Patrick Manson.* London: Cassel and Co., 1927; Manson-Bahr, Philip. *Patrick Manson: The Father of Tropical Medicine.* London, 1962; and Pantoja, Enrique. "A Heritage Map of Medical London." *Medicine's Geographic Heritage* 1989; 5: 47-56. By 1904, Manson's fame was spreading around the world. In the words of Charles Morrow Wilson, *Ambassadors in White*, op.cit., "It was an era of imperialism and Sir Patrick Manson had taken the lead proclaiming that tropical medicine was as profitable as it was interesting.": 165.
36   Manson-Bahr, Philip. *History of the School of Tropical Medicine in London,* 1899-1949, London: Lewis, 1956: 188.
37   Ibid.: 121.
38   Papers of Francis W. O'Connor, Historical Collections, New York Academy of Medicine, essay titled "Manson and Ross," September 16, 1932. O'Connor wrote this essay on the occasion of the death of Sir Ronald Ross. The handwritten manuscript has no numbered pages. This source will be hereafter referred to as "Manson and Ross," NYAM.
39   "Manson and Ross," NYAM.
40   Ibid.

colleague "McDougal," thereby not only divesting him of his Irish heritage but also making him an honorary Scot.[41]

O'Connor was a frequent guest at the Mansons' home in London as well as at their fishing lodge in Galway, thus allowing the two men to share their hopes and life's work and to discuss possible avenues for research. It is therefore not surprising that O'Connor relied on the counsel of his older colleague, whom he felt was gifted with "great broad imaginings and fully prophetic powers."[42] Moreover, Manson was generous to a fault with his ideas, giving "most lavishly of his theories and hypotheses"[43] and dismissing all claims to fame and wealth. O'Connor was also impressed by the fact that Manson was, until the end of his life, a determined, driven worker who never gave up the quest for discovery, either by himself or through his pupils.

But Manson was more than a mentor to O'Connor, for the young Irishman fell in love with Manson's daughter Edith Margaret and therefore saw the elder scholar as a potential father-in-law. The romantic attachment proved to be one-sided. O'Connor soon found himself outmaneuvered and outwitted by Philip Bahr, a parasitologist who had also apprenticed himself to "Mosquito Manson" and successfully

---

41   Ibid.
42   Ibid.
43   Ibid.

wooed the fair maiden.[44] In 1909 Edith made her choice and married Bahr, leaving O'Connor heart-broken.

Given the tension between Manson's two protégés, O'Connor knew that he had to make a graceful exit. Being Irish in an English world, he surmised that his chances of furthering his career in London were, in his words, "so slim as to be nonexistent."[45] So he chose to join the medical sleuths whom Great Britain sent abroad to do research and report on its far-flung empire. In 1910 O'Connor went to Formosa as part of an expedition organized by Manson.

The extended stay in Formosa gave O'Connor exposure to the field of helminthology and to several prominent Japanese researchers who had made significant findings in identifying pathogenic river flukes. Upon his return to London in 1911, O'Connor was described by his former rival as "brimming over with enthusiasm" at current

---

44   Kean, B.H., with Tracy Daily. *MD: One Doctor's Adventures Among the Famous and Infamous from the Jungles of Panama to a Park Avenue Practice.* New York, NY: Ballantine Books, 1990: 20.

45   At that time, the "Irish question" (i.e., how to address the growing clamor for self-government in Ireland) occupied center stage in parliament. The Liberal government's failure to introduce a Home Rule bill for Ireland in 1906 fostered the rise of Sinn Fein, a radical national movement that is still active. In 1911 the Liberals agreed to introduce legislation for Home Rule, but met with the violent opposition of those who felt that this would subvert "civil and religious freedom." Positions for and against granting Ireland greater sovereignty became increasingly polarized, and by 1914 it was felt that Ireland was on the verge of civil war. This was deflected by World War I. Nevertheless, two central issues that had to be defused in order to address the "Irish question"—the refusal of Ulster to join an independent Ireland, and of the Irish nationalists to accept the partition of Ireland—remained unresolved. Thompson, P. *The Edwardians*, op. cit.: 263-265.

research developments in the Far East. However dejected he may have felt prior to his self-styled 'exile,' O'Connor now returned with new knowledge as well as with the boundless energy and "that *joie de vivre* which was so characteristic of an Irishman."[46] Being then "in the prime of life, vivacious, pugnacious, an enthusiast and a great talker," he found himself as a demonstrator[47] and an assistant entomologist in the London School of Tropical Medicine, where he was once more guided by Sir Patrick Manson, this time with the assistance of entomologist Alfred Alcock.[48]

With such distinguished mentors, O'Connor was in the best possible environment in which to develop his clinical and research interests. Accordingly, he "infiltrated every department, picking up gems here and there, but paying most attention to protozoology and medical entomology."[49] He became particularly friendly with Alcock, whose department

---

46   Manson-Bahr, P. *History of the School of Tropical Medicine*, op cit.: 188. While chronicling the history of the School of Tropical Medicine in London, Manson-Bahr was remarkably complimentary in his description of O'Connor. O'Connor had once publicly called him a "hyphenated Hun," a reference to Manson-Bahr's German background as well as to the fact that he had altered his last name to add that of his wife and his famous father-in-law. [See Kean, B.H. MD, op.cit.: 20]. While clearly claiming Sir Patrick Manson's mantle, Philip Manson-Bahr was also following the practice espoused by the British royal family. During the anti-German atmosphere of World War I, George V declared that all descendants of Queen Victoria in the male line would henceforth go by the surname "Windsor" rather than by their own dynastic name of Saxe-Coburg-Gotha. Similarly, the Battenbergs became the "Mountbattens."

47   The title of "demonstrator" is the equivalent of the position of teaching assistant/laboratory technician in medical schools today.

48   Manson-Bahr, P. *History of the School of Tropical Medicine*, op. cit.: 188.

49   Ibid.

he enriched with the Eastern specimens he had collected while in Formosa.[50] But his teaching activities also allowed quite a bit of formal training, and he completed the requirements toward the Diploma of Tropical Medicine in 1913.[51]

World War I

O'Connor was at the School of Tropical Medicine when his commitment to the academic life gave way to the needs of war service. Although he was an Irish nationalist at heart, he espoused the Allied cause wholeheartedly.[52] In 1914, O'Connor was therefore part of the massive mobilization that affected all of Britain. The war effort required that all men be drafted to military service or be assigned to industries and other tasks that were considered essential work. Whether equipped with Sten guns or stethoscopes, tanks or test tubes, Great Britain's men were expected to serve in whatever capacity they could best defend their country.

Like many others, O'Connor got married sometime prior to heeding the call to arms. His bride was Zella Otto, whom he had met on the SS Armadale Castle when she was on her way to Durban, South Africa. She was a beautiful

---

50   Ibid.

51   The DTM, which was actually granted by Cambridge University, is indicated in the credentials listed when he was under consideration for an appointment at Columbia 15 years later. Minutes, Committee on Administration, College of Physicians and Surgeons, Columbia University, May 28, 1928. Archives and Special Collections, A. C. Long Library, Columbia University, New York.

52   Manson-Bahr, P. *History of the School of Tropical Medicine*, op.cit.: 188.

and talented pianist who was willing to cast her lot with someone whose future was uncertain yet promising.[53]

The war in many places was a "war of germs rather than of guns," and the faculty of the School of Tropical Medicine was soon scattered over many fronts.[54] O'Connor's first assignment was in France, where he was a medical officer on ambulance train Number 10.[55] In 1915 he was sent to Egypt and Palestine, joining protozoologist Charles Morley Wenyon in Alexandria in early 1916. There, they moved into tents to survey the vast array of Egyptian protozoa waging their own war with the intestinal tracts of the British troops. Their methods of collecting specimens were as simple as they were effective:

> O'Connor issued each homesick soldier an empty wooden latrine bucket. Along with the receptacle each man received an ultimatum approved by the military

53   There is limited information on the circumstances leading to the marriage, which is surprising given the rather detailed record of much of O'Connor's life. His wife and family appear to have been tangential and even incidental to his life and career. Yet the account of his life written in 1922 was aimed at his children, one of whom was only 4 years of age at the time. In this account, O'Connor acknowledged that "owing to the unhappy circumstances of my relationship with your mother, you will probably see little of me." Still, the marriage was apparently never dissolved, and his will recognized the existence of a wife, Zella O'Connor, living in Natal, South Africa.

54   Indeed, several who served on the War Office's Medical Advisory Committee were referred to as a "Travelling Circus" because they toured the different fronts and advised on tropical diseases. Manson-Bahr, P. *History of the School of Tropical Medicine*, op.cit.: 57.

55   FWO (Francis W. O'Connor) Diary excerpt, May 5, 1925. Record Group 12.1, Box 50. Rockefeller Foundation Archives, Rockefeller Archives Center, Sleepy Hollow, New York (hereafter designated RAC).

high command: fill the bucket and return home to England, refuse and stay in Egypt. "You can be sure," O'Connor said [...], "that the soldiers were literally over-flowing with enthusiasm."[56]

Combining their considerable investigative skills with this abundance of clinical material, Wenyon and O'Connor were able to describe several new species of intestinal protozoa and a new human intestinal flagellate. During this research, O'Connor accidentally infected himself with ancylostomes, an infection which caused him great distress.[57]

In August 1917, O'Connor was back in England, reunited with his family.[58] He held the rank of Captain in the Royal Army Medical Corps, and was working for the War Office, charged with the epidemiological surveillance of the rising number of malaria cases among the British servicemen. He reported the finding of locally-acquired malaria near Tilbury Dock, and the War Office wanted confirmation. They sent Sir Ronald Ross, then a consultant in malariology to the War Office, to check O'Connor's finding.[59] Ross was uniquely qualified for the task: building on Manson's hypothesis that malaria was mosquito-borne, Ross had discovered that malaria can be transmitted from infected mosquitoes as they bite healthy hosts. This discovery laid to rest centuries of belief in miasma, or decaying organic matter, as the cause of this

---

56   Kean, B.H. *MD*, op.cit.: 20-21.

57   Manson-Bahr, P. A *History of the School of Tropical Medicine*, op.cit.: 188.

58   "God is good, I am with my Darling again," he wrote in his diary. Excerpt dated August 17, 1917 in Francis W. O'Connor Diary #3, November 25, 1915 to November 25, 1917. NYAM.

59   "Manson and Ross," NYAM.

disease.[60] Ross's finding was considered a major breakthrough in the prevention and treatment of this potentially deadly disease, earning him the Nobel Prize for Medicine in 1902. He was also awarded an endowed chair at the Liverpool School of Tropical Medicine that same year, a knighthood in 1911, and honors from the Belgian government.[61]

At Tilbury, Ross promptly confirmed O'Connor's diagnoses. A few days later, O'Connor was sent to Sandwich, a medieval town located in Kent, England, to investigate a supposed outbreak of malaria among recruits. There he found that the condition was much more widespread than originally reported: there were 31 cases of malaria among the troops, as well as numerous breeding places in close proximity to the

---

60   Of course, not everyone was willing to relinquish the miasmatic theory of malaria causation. Thus, for example, the Legislative Council of Barbados passed a resolution that "it was against the will of God and that the very idea that mosquitoes carried malaria to man was blasphemous as it was not written in the Bible." Quoted in Manson-Bahr, P. and Alcock, A. *Life and Work*, op. cit.: 99.

61   In addition, Ross was the author of *Prevention of Malaria* and had pioneered the use of mathematical models in epidemiology. Ross, Ronald. Memoirs. London: John Murray, 1923. Despite his accomplishments and the widespread recognition they brought him, Ross came to regard Manson as a competitor in the primacy of the etiology of malaria, and began a petty feud that did not end until both their deaths. Still, Manson never said anything acrimonious about his one-time protégé, and indeed stated that his greatest discovery was discovering Ronald Ross. The one-sided bitter rivalry between the two men is described in Guillemin, Jeanne. "Choosing Scientific Patrimony: Sir Ronald Ross, Alphonse Laveran, and the Mosquito-Vector Hypothesis for Malaria." *Journal of the History of Medicine and Allied Sciences* 2002; 57 (4): 385-409. Writing in 1932, O'Connor stated that, as far as he could ascertain, he was the only person who had worked intimately with both Manson and Ross, and felt that, while Manson was "a giant," Ross was over-rated. "Manson and Ross," NYAM.

military encampments.[62] Ross was once again dispatched to confirm the situation, and he agreed with the findings. Indeed, the noted parasitologist was quite impressed with O'Connor's diagnostic acumen and epidemiological skills, and requested that the Irishman be assigned to his staff.[63]

Within three weeks, O'Connor found himself a staff officer reporting directly to Sir Ronald Ross. His first assignment was to survey all the officers in charge of malaria control within two military commands, and to report his findings as an abstract for publication.[64] After this, he joined Ross on an extended trip to consult with the Department of Medical Services regarding malaria among the English troops in Macedonia.[65] They traveled through France and Italy to Salonika, where Ross remained. O'Connor was dispatched to the Struma area, where the outbreak of malaria was particularly severe.[66] The marshy banks of the Struma River, extending from Bulgaria into Greece, harbored malarial mosquitoes, against which the

---

62   O'Connor, F.W. (Captain, RAMC), "Report on Indigenous Malaria Occurring Amongst Troops in England," (n.d., late 1917 or early 1918). Papers of Sir Ronald Ross, Archives, London School of Hygiene and Tropical Medicine (hereafter designated RR/LSHTP).

63   Hill, Francis R. To The General Officer, Commanding-in-Chief, Eastern Command, October 16, 1917. RR/LSHTM.

64   Ross, Ronald. Handwritten note, November 2, 1917. RR/LSHTM.

65   Leaving his family was difficult for O'Connor. His son was quite ill, and he left "in a state of miserable despair." In his diary, he noted: "It is awful leaving my Darling Girl with this strait. She is so brave and I hate to think of my impatience at her opposing my plans which are all for her interest and the children." Excerpt dated September 7, 1917, Francis W. O'Connor Diary #3, November 25, 1915-November 25, 1917. NYAM.

66   "Manson and Ross," NYAM.

available preventive measures proved ineffectual.[67] As a result, the troops were decimated, the overwhelming majority of them suffering from malaria. During the Salonika campaign, for every casualty of battle, three died because of malaria, influenza, or other diseases.[68] Following this campaign, Ross and O'Connor returned to London to the War Office.

In spring of 1918, O'Connor fell ill and was "invalided." This status earned him an extended medical leave, his return to war duties being contingent on passing a physical examination. While his letters include no explicit mention of his condition, his symptoms suggest that it was mental as well as physical. The treatment consisted primarily of "getting fresh air" and rest, although Ross counseled O'Connor to give up smoking cigarettes and become a teetotaler for a time.

O'Connor spent much of his convalescence in Ireland, at the Mansons' lodge in Galway. While he rested, he was not idle. In addition to fishing for trout, he wrote reviews for the journal *Nature*, drafted a paper on his work in Egypt,[69] and worried about his future career prospects. He was particularly

---

67   These measures included pouring cresol in pools to kill the larvae and personal protection against mosquitoes. In the words of F.A.W. Nash, one witness who was part of the RAMC's contingent in Salonika: "The night patrols had a ritual of their own. Each man anointed his face and neck with almond-smelling mixture of the appearance of floor polish. This was to make us unpleasant to the mosquitoes. Then we put on a muslin veil and tucked the loose ends into our tunics." Quoted in *The Long, Long Trail: The Story of the British Army in the Great War of 1914-1918*." See: http://www.1914-1918.net/salonika.htm.

68   *The Long, Long Trail*. One army nurse reporting on the conditions in the front lines in Salonika said that "Out of 500, sometimes they have only about 95 men—all the rest are down here with malaria." *The Diary of Mrs. Edith Moor*. See: http://www.salonika.freeserve.co.uk/NurseInSalonika.htm.

69   O'Connor, F.W. Intestine Protozoa. Statistics. (n.d.)

concerned that, while the war efforts of many colleagues had been recognized, he was the only worker in tropical medicine whose labors had not received a "mention." He knew that his work with Wenyon in Egypt had been submitted for recognition, and expressed disappointment that nothing had come of this. Nevertheless, he concluded that, once he was better, he would have to "try to win [his] spurs on some other expeditionary field."[70]

O'Connor joined his wife and met his newborn son in Sussex in May 1918, spending the rest of his medical leave with his family.[71] By early July he was ready to return to work; he hoped that the War Office would send him abroad both because the pay was greater and because he felt that home service was "more than useless for one's prospects."[72] His preference was to return to Salonika, where he would rejoin Wenyon, or to Egypt.[73]

But, after he was declared medically fit, O'Connor was instead assigned to special malaria work in the Shorncliffe District of England.[74] He apparently stayed there until armistice in November 1918. Once the war was over, both he and Ross were appointed consultants in tropical medicine to the Appeals Board of the Ministry of Pensions.[75]

---

70   O'Connor, F.W. to Sir Ronald Ross, April 4, 1918. RR/LSHTM.

71   His son had been born "a few days ago," while O'Connor was in Galway.
O'Connor, F. W. to Sir Ronald Ross, May 23, 1918. RR/LSHTM.

72   O'Connor, F.W. Letter to Sir Ronald Ross, May 30, 1918. RR/LSHTM.

73   Ross, Ronald. Note on conversation with O'Connor, June 14, 1918. RR/LSHTM.

74   Ross, Ronald. Letter to F.W. O'Connor, July 2, 1918. RR/LSHTM.

75   "Manson and Ross." NYAM.

Earning His Spurs

Following demobilization, O'Connor returned to the School of Tropical Medicine in London. The research efforts that had been curtailed during the war had resumed, and the School was eager to become active overseas.[76] Almost immediately Sir Patrick Manson commissioned O'Connor to go on an extended and far-flung expedition: to study filariasis in the Ellice, Tokelau, and Samoan Islands. The trip was motivated by a statement made by a medical officer of the Gilbert and Ellice Islands asserting the efficacy of salvarsan[77] in treating filariasis. The expedition thus sought to "combine an investigation of this statement by experimental methods with a general survey of these little-known islands from the medical standpoint."[78]

With the official title of "Wandsworth Scholar of the School of Tropical Medicine," O'Connor, accompanied by an assistant and a volunteer, sailed eastward on October 18, 1919, reaching the Ellice Islands in April 1920. He was to remain there for a total of 17 months, surveying the population of twenty islands.[79] The research team tested not only salvarsan, but also a number of other preparations that were then used to treat filariasis. They found that none of the drugs, "by

---

76   *Manson-Bahr, P. History of the School of Tropical Medicine*, op cit.: 66.

77   Salvarsan is the trade name for arsphenamine, a drug used in the treatment of syphilis and trypanosomiasis. This compound is recognized as the first true chemotherapeutic agent, and was discovered in 1908 by Sahachiro Hata while at Paul Erlich's laboratory.

78   O'Connor, F.W. "Researches in the Western Pacific: Being a Report on the Results of the Expedition sent from the London School of Tropical Medicine to the Ellice, Tokelaun, and Samoan Islands in 1921-22." *Res Mem Lond Sch Trop Med* 1923; 4: 57.

79   Ibid.: 2.

whatsoever method administered...[had] any effect on the numbers, behaviour, or structure of the microfilariae in the bloodstream," although some had a mitigating effect on symptoms, most likely as a result of the bodily rest required by the treatment.[80] Moreover, treatment was found to be difficult among the populations studied: "They look for a miraculous cure, and depart when it does not happen, and they intensely dislike operations, though in no instance did sepsis or any local complications follow our injections."[81] Upon his return, O'Connor published his report, which confirmed and extended the work that had brought worldwide recognition to Manson more than 25 years earlier.

In England, O'Connor was once again looking for a new adventure, or at least for a change of venue. Although he was unaware of it at the time, 1922 proved to be another "year of destiny" in which external events shaped his future. In April of that year Manson died. O'Connor thus lost a friend and protector, a mentor and an inspiration. Whatever distress he may have felt at this loss was exacerbated by concerns over his own health and the state of his marriage. Although only 38 at the time, he felt that his life would be cut short. He therefore penned his memoirs in order to leave his children a history of their forebears and an account of his life.[82] By then his marriage was a formality, and little more.[83] While having financial obligations, he was relatively unencumbered by emotional or family ties.

---

80   Ibid.: 24.
81   Ibid.: 24.
82   This is the account, dated July 30, 1922, which is available at the NYAM.
83   See Note 53.

Absent Manson's support, O'Connor sought other allies in the 'corridors of power.' With the backing of entomologist Alfred Alcock, O'Connor applied to and was accepted as a Fellow of the Royal Society of Tropical Medicine and Hygiene.[84] And another *deus ex machina* soon materialized, offering the possibility of a new beginning. O'Connor came to the attention of Dr. Victor Heiser, an American physician who was then scouring the world for "enthusiastic seekers after knowledge" and research scientists to recruit for the programs of the Rockefeller Foundation's International Health Board (IHB).[85] The Foundation was devoting an increasing share of its considerable resources to the eradication of disease, part of its campaign "for the good of mankind."[86] O'Connor was asked to work in the area of malaria control, then a priority not only in the southern states of the United States but throughout the world. With his credentials in tropical medicine, his war experience, and a strong recommendation from none other than Sir Ronald Ross,[87] O'Connor was a likely prospect to join the Foundation in its global campaign to cast off disease.

---

84   Candidate for Admission as Fellow of the Society, Royal Society of Tropical Medicine and Hygiene, submitted November 11, 1922, elected December 21, 1922. Application provided courtesy of the Royal Society of Tropical Medicine and Hygiene.

85   RMP (Richard M. Pearce) Diary Excerpt, Record Group 12.1, Box 51. Rockefeller Archive Center, Sleepy Hollow, New York (hereafter designated as RAC). Heiser (1873-1972) devoted his life to the study and treatment of tropical diseases. Heiser, Victor. *An American Doctor's Odyssey: Adventures in 45 Countries.* New York: W. W. Norton and Co., 1936.

86   Farley, John. *To Cast Off Disease: A History of the International Health Division of Rockefeller Foundation (1913-1951).* Oxford: Oxford University Press, 2004.

87   O'Connor, F.W. to Sir Ronald Ross, December 21, 1922. RR/LSHTM. O'Connor thanks Ross for "the practical testimonial…which I know will be of great assistance to me."

By early 1923, he thus found himself sailing for New York on the SS America.[88] His commitment was for one year, subject to the needs of the IHB. During that time he did research on malaria and other mosquito-borne diseases, writing two reports, "Animal Barrier Investigation," and a "Preliminary Report on the Anophelines of Lee County, Georgia."[89] At the end of the year, however, he had no permanent position to go back to. He was thus considering returning to England, possibly to a take up obstetrics and anesthesiology as general training for private practice.[90]

A week before sailing back to England, a chance conversation with Dr. Richard M. Pearce, director of the Rockefeller Foundation's Division of Medical Education (DME), resulted in a tentative job offer and a marked change of plans. Stopping by to see O'Connor "as a matter of courtesy," Pearce ended up giving serious consideration to hiring him as Assistant Director of the DME. In his diary notes, Pearce sized up O'Connor's capabilities and the rationale for his proposal:

> RMP is inclined to think that O'Connor may be considered very seriously for…[the] DME. Irish with an English training, graduate of Bart's, he has had 15 years experience in teaching, research, and field services in tropical medicine, with experience in the London School of Tropical Medicine. Apparently he has fulfilled all tasks assigned to him satisfactorily, but has never been able to find a permanent position. […] There is no question about his ability to carry out a

---

88   Ibid.

89   The former is dated 1923; the latter, 1924. Both are on file as part of Record Group 1.1, series 100i, box 50, RAC.

90   RMP Diary Excerpt for January 16, 1924. RAC.

piece of work satisfactorily under direction. [...] He has a good personality, pleasant manner, is apparently tactful and diplomatic, obviously a gentleman. With his wide experience in various parts of the world, especially the Far East, it might be possible for him to master the principles of medical education and be of service to the DME.[91]

The matter of O'Connor's family situation came up in the conversation with Pearce. While acknowledging that he was married and had three children, O'Connor stated that his wife and children were living in Natal, South Africa, and that the separation that had already lasted several years was likely "to be made permanent."[92] Still, Pearce was reassured that O'Connor had "done his duty by the family, sending every possible penny to his wife for their support."[93]

After consulting with his superiors in the Foundation, Pearce offered O'Connor the position of assistant to the Director of the DME for one year, with a salary of $5,000.[94] It was understood that the appointment was temporary, with no commitment as to reappointment. O'Connor accepted readily, expressing great satisfaction at the prospect of becoming better

---

91   Ibid.

92   Indeed, in a diary note addressed to his wife Zella and dated October 1923, O'Connor wrote as follows: "You know that you maligned and slandered me to my influential friends. You slurred me against them on your own behalf [...] You were faithless and false to me from the start. Thus have you treated a man whose only guilt was his love for you and thus have you dragged down beyond hope of uprising a man who sold his very soul and all he held dear for your sake." Diary recapitulation for the month of October, 1923. Diary of Francis W. O'Connor, 1923. NYAM.

93   RMP Diary Excerpt for January 16, 1924. RAC.

94   This is the equivalent of $56,000 in current dollars.

acquainted with American medicine as well as with the work of the Rockefeller Foundation, familiarity with these being valuable no matter what his future work would be.[95]

A Rockefeller Officer

As a short-term perch from which to survey and possibly shape the medical scene, O'Connor's new position had a number of advantages. First, he was representing a major foundation whose largesse was legendary;[96] this gave him immediate entry into the worlds of research and academe. Secondly, the Foundation's international reach meant that O'Connor would gain exposure to issues of similar scope. Foundation officers were expected to keep abreast of global developments in their area of expertise. In addition, Foundation officers had a number of perquisites by virtue of the Rockefeller name: they traveled well, were well received wherever they went, and they commanded an instant respect that others would have had to earn. With the Foundation's many projects related to tropical medicine, O'Connor would be apprised of any opportunities that opened up in the field. Lastly, program officers quickly became part of an "old boy network" that gave them access to the leading scholars and decision-makers in the health field. In due course, O'Connor would reap the benefits of all these 'perks.'

The Division of Medical Education sought to transform

---

95   RMP Diary Excerpt of January 25, 1924. RAC.

96   Although the Rockefeller name had originally "reeked of oil and all its unpleasant connotations," the philanthropic enterprises that were associated with it would soon reap dividends in terms of prestige and reputation. Heiser, V. *An American Doctor's Odyssey*, op.cit.: 272.

the teaching of medicine and nursing by promoting the inclusion of more sciences as part of the medical curriculum. It also supported the research of U.S. scholars who wished to go abroad, and of foreign researchers doing fellowships in the United States. It was therefore constantly matching researchers and institutions, finding appropriate mentors for young scholars, and monitoring the progress of the research thus generated.

Because the Rockefeller dollars were instrumental in bolstering the finances and reputations of many medical schools, university presidents and medical school deans were intent on currying favor with the program officers who could sway the Foundation's decisions on the allocation of resources. These officers commanded a great deal of attention among the institutions they visited. Invariably, these were the universities that were at the forefront of medical teaching and research; their faculties therefore read like a "who's who" of academic medicine.[97] Not surprisingly, O'Connor was soon caught in a whirlwind of site visits, social activities, consultations, and meetings. His work diary, which contains brief notes on all encounters and telephone calls, reflects the activities that shaped his day.[98] For example, within three days during the week of February 7, 1925, his calendar included witnessing a

---

97   Among the names mentioned in O'Connor's diary notes are those of Doctors Walter Cannon, Harvey Cushing, David Edsall, Carlos Finlay, Austin Flint, Raymond Pearl, and William H. Welch, among many others.

98   This reflects the prevailing protocol at the Rockefeller Foundation, with all program officers keeping similar records of their activities. The use of the third person, the type of annotation, and the typing and eventual binding of the diary notes are all part of the Foundation's modus operandi.

demonstration of a new technology allowing users to dissect and inject individual cells under a microscope; having lunch with Mrs. John D. Rockefeller, Jr.; meeting with Dr. Robert A. Lambert to discuss the still-evolving "Porto Rico Tropical School"; and teaching at Mount Sinai Hospital at the bedside of a patient with a liver abscess.[99] In addition to this exposure to many persons and events, the position also allowed O'Connor to travel widely, visiting Rockefeller Fellows and medical faculty in Boston, New Haven, Baltimore, Chicago, Montreal, and Toronto, among many other medical meccas.

As O'Connor became increasingly immersed in the cultures of the Rockefeller Foundation and American medical schools, his portfolio expanded accordingly. He worked closely with Pearce and attempted to correlate the work of the DME with that of the General Education Board, another Rockefeller division also involved in the reform of medical education. He had responsibilities over schools in both the United States and Europe, and was assigned the task of preparing bulletins for publication.[100] After the year ended, O'Connor's contract was extended and his assignments were broadened. By 1927, he was handling all of the DME's routine correspondence in the areas of medical education and human biology, supervising all of the division's fellowships in medicine, and producing the DME's annual report.[101] In addition, he was the editor and compiler of a publication titled "Methods and Problems of Medical Education," which addressed topics that cut across

99   FWO (Francis W. O'Connor) Diary Excerpts for February 7-9, 1925. RAC.
100   RMP Diaries, Excerpt for April 29, 1924. RAC.
101   Ibid., Excerpt for April 1, 1927. RAC.

medical schools and aimed to publicize "best practices" in all aspects of medical education.[102]

These activities brought O'Connor into contact with institutions throughout the United States and, indeed, throughout the world. This in turn enhanced his job prospects. In 1927 he was approached about joining the University of Texas in Galveston as dean and professor of medicine. In his diary notes, O'Connor noted that, while he was interested in a position in tropical medicine, parasitology, or preventive medicine in the tropics, preferably one primarily involving research, he was not inclined towards any job where the emphasis was on administration, as would be the case in Texas.[103] He thus rejected the tentative offer.

Puerto Rican Interlude

Soon after this offer, he was invited by Dr. Robert A. Lambert to go to Puerto Rico as a visiting lecturer at the School of Tropical Medicine. This he readily accepted after consulting Pearce and receiving his approval.[104] The understanding was that O'Connor would be on leave from the Foundation sometime in the fall of 1927, and that he would be paid by the School.[105]

In fact, however, O'Connor's honorarium and travel expenses were covered by the Rockefeller Foundation. Even before the school had opened in Puerto Rico, the International

---

102   See, for example, *Methods and Problems of Medical Education*. New York, NY: Division of Medical Education, The Rockefeller Foundation, 1927. This covers the topics of medical records, libraries in medical schools, and sanitary surveys.

103   FWO Diary Excerpt for March 21, 1927. RAC

104   FWO Diary Excerpt for July 21, 1927; and RMP Diary Excerpt for July 21, 1927. RAC.

105   Ibid.

Health Board had agreed to give Columbia the sum of $8,000 to support visiting professorships at the fledgling enterprise, thereby encouraging the intellectual cross-pollination to which the Foundation was committed.[106] Once the school opened its doors, its ties to the Rockefeller Foundation were bolstered by its director, who had close ties to the Foundation. In 1922 Lambert had delivered a series of lectures at the University of Salvador (Brazil) under the auspices of the Foundation, and made a survey of medical education in Central America for the IHB. The following year the Foundation had hired him for the Faculty of Medicine of Sao Paulo, where he served as professor of pathology until he became director of the School of Tropical Medicine of the University of Puerto Rico.[107]

When he invited O'Connor to lecture in Puerto Rico, Lambert was considering leaving the island the following year. By then the school would be "in good shape," and he was not interested in continuing.[108] He was therefore open to the possibility of a position with the Division of Medical Education at the Rockefeller Foundation, which Pearce suggested.[109] For O'Connor, the invitation presented a welcome change from the administrative routine. It also provided an opportunity to become involved in academic research once again. The limited knowledge he had about Puerto Rico promised a congenial tropical environment: the island combined the exuberant nature he had experienced in the Canary Islands with the varied pathology he had found in the South Seas. Moreover, he had some acquaintance with the prevailing epidemiological picture,

---

106   RMP Diary Excerpt of September 19, 1924. RAC.

107   Appointments, *Rockefeller Foundation Quarterly Bulletin* 1928; 2 (2): 176.

108   RMP Diary Excerpt of May 25, 1927. RAC.

109   Ibid.

and was familiar with the findings of colleagues who had spent extended periods on the island. H.J. Johnson, who had spent a year doing a survey of malaria in Puerto Rico for the IHB, had found a high prevalence of infection without much evidence of the disease. He had also found that filariasis and elephantiasis seemed to be concentrated on the western part of the island, a finding that O'Connor felt was very significant and worthy of careful investigation.[110]

The presence of the School of Tropical Medicine was undoubtedly a goad to research. Inaugurated with great fanfare only a year earlier, the School capitalized on the prestige of Columbia University and the political legitimacy of the University of Puerto Rico. It attracted both seasoned researchers and those who were embarking on careers in tropical medicine.[111] As its first director, Dr. Robert A. Lambert felt that, of the School's two functions—teaching and research—it would be the latter that would not only have the most valuable results but also "carry the name of the School over the world."[112] He therefore recruited known researchers and scientists who would lecture at the School. During its first year, the School had welcomed an impressive roster of guest lecturers, including Dr. Simon Flexner of the Rockefeller Institute for Medical Research, Dr. Juan Iturbe of the Faculty of Medicine in Caracas, and Dr. Martha May

---

110   FWO Diary Excerpt of March 11, 1925. RAC.

111   Ramírez de Arellano, Annette B. "Columbia's Overseas Venture: The School of Tropical Medicine at the University of Puerto Rico." *Medicine's Geographic Heritage* 1989; 5: 35-40.

112   Lambert, Robert A. "Preliminary Report of the Director of the School of Tropical Medicine, 1926-1927.": 3. Record Group 1.1, Series 243, Box 2, Folder 28. RAC.

Eliot of Yale University and the U.S. Department of Labor's Children's Bureau. Lambert could therefore correctly state that "probably never before [had] Puerto Rico had the opportunity of seeing and hearing so many distinguished visitors in a single season."[113]

O'Connor was therefore in good company, something he was sure to appreciate. While his lecture schedule was not very demanding—he was to give three scientific lectures at the School and two 'popular' lectures in San Juan and Ponce over the course of three weeks—O'Connor was also provided with opportunities for field investigation on filariasis.[114] His interest in this disease, initially encouraged by Manson and developed during his expeditions to Formosa and Polynesia, was further whetted by the many questions that remained to be answered. While clearly recognized as mosquito-borne, filariasis and its natural history remained a puzzle. For example, it was not known how the microfilaria entered the host's bloodstream, nor was there any certainty concerning the longevity of the parasite in the human body. In addition, while seasonal and even diurnal patterns in the prevalence of the pathogenic agent had been established, there was no information on why this periodicity occurred.[115] Studying this disease in a high-

---

113   Ibid.

114   The three scientific lectures included two on filariasis and one on amebic dysentery; the popular lectures were on his researches in the South Sea Islands. Lambert, Robert A. "Report of the Director to the Special Board of Trustees for the year ending June 30, 1928." School of Tropical Medicine of the University of Puerto Rico under the auspices of Columbia University: 3. RAC.

115   O'Connor, F.W. "Filariasis in association with infection of *Filaria Bancrofti.*" *Porto Rico Review of Public Health and Tropical Medicine* 1927; III (6): 211-222.

prevalence area such as Puerto Rico was therefore particularly attractive to the visiting lecturer, who was always on the lookout for fertile terrain for potential investigations.

At the same time that he was laying the groundwork for future activities, O'Connor was expected to take part in a number of visits and social events. He was, after all, playing many roles—foreign guest, physician, visiting professor, researcher, foundation officer—any one of which would have made him worthy of special consideration. But combined in a single individual, these titles assured O'Connor a lavish display of Puerto Rican hospitality. He was wined, dined, and feted during his entire sojourn. Whether having tea with the Governor's wife at La Fortaleza, given flowers by the nursing staff of a hospital in Ponce, or taken to lunch at the Union Club,[116] O'Connor was lionized by his hosts and colleagues.

His travel diary speaks for itself, and will not be summarized here. In equal parts an *aide-mémoire*, an activities report, and a recapitulation of the writer's thoughts at the end of the day, O'Connor's chronicle reflects an outsider's view of the island at a time of great effervescence in the health field. It thus captures the newness and excitement that permeated the initiatives of the mid-1920s, when public concerns and private financing converged to strengthen and expand health services. While the construction of the imposing citadel housing the School of Tropical Medicine was the most obvious symbol of the importance accorded the public's health, it was by no means the only major achievement. The years 1923 to 1926 had seen the opening of a clinic devoted to social hygiene and

---

116   A social civic club established by North Americans in Miramar, San Juan, in 1908.

sexually transmitted diseases in San Juan, the inauguration in Río Piedras of the first public health unit, the planning of a 1000-bed Psychiatric Hospital, and the establishment of the *Puerto Rico Health Review*.[117] It is therefore likely that O'Connor would perceive the optimism and sense of possibilities that suffused Puerto Rico at the time of his visit. Not surprisingly, he made it a point to begin research that would ensure return visits in years to come.

By the time he returned to New York at the end of 1927, O'Connor was ready to leave the Rockefeller Foundation for an academic position. Prior to his trip, he had already had conversations with Dr. W.W. Palmer, Professor of Medicine at Columbia's College of Physicians and Surgeons, about the possibility of a full-time academic appointment, teaching and overseeing all research in tropical medicine.[118] Although Dr. Bailey K. Ashford had expressed interest in an affiliation with Columbia for three months each year, resources were limited and the likelihood of both men being hired was remote. Palmer's plans for O'Connor meant that Ashford's proposal would not go forward. Within a week after returning from Puerto Rico, O'Connor had successfully concluded his negotiations with Palmer and accepted the position at Columbia.[119]

Before leaving the Division of Medical Education, however, O'Connor was charged with a final task that must have been very much to his liking both as a wrap-up to his Rockefeller years and as a prelude to his new position: he was to "observe developments in teaching and research at the various

---

117   Costa Mandry, Oscar. *Apuntes para la Historia de la Medicina en Puerto Rico.* San Juan, PR, 1971: 130.

118   RMP Diary Excerpt of November 21, 1927. RAC.

119   RMP Diary Excerpt of November 26, 1927. RAC.

institutes of parasitology and tropical medicine in Europe."[120] Starting with one of his former training grounds, renamed the London School of Hygiene and Tropical Medicine, he also visited the Liverpool School of Tropical Medicine, Cambridge University, and the recently inaugurated Ross Institute and Hospital for Tropical Diseases, where he renewed his ties with Sir Ronald Ross, whom he had not seen since demobilization. In England O'Connor also visited the Wellcome Bureau of Scientific Research, then directed by C. M. Wenyon, with whom he had worked in Egypt. His survey also covered the Military Academy in Marseilles, the Institut Pasteur in Algiers, two Dutch institutes (in Amsterdam and Leiden), and the schools of tropical medicine in Brussels and Hamburg.[121]

In his final report, O'Connor indicated that all schools recognized the importance of having field stations where their researchers could study tropical diseases in endemic areas.[122] He also found consensus concerning three major needs: keeping training in tropical medicine at the postgraduate level, teaching ethnology, and having a hospital adjacent to the school to insure the timely observation of the course of tropical diseases.[123] Now that O'Connor was to join the beneficiaries of the Rockefeller Foundation, he concluded with a plea for

---

120 O'Connor, F.W. "The Teaching of Tropical Medicine in Europe." *Rockefeller Foundation Quarterly Bulletin* 1929; 2 (3): 195-224; 195.

121 Ibid.

122 Ibid.: 222, In his diary notes, O'Connor wrote that his visits convinced him "of the importance of such field stations as the Institut Pasteur in Algiers and Tunis, and the Tropical School in Porto Rico. There seems to be no doubt whatever that more research in tropical diseases is done at such institutes than at any of the institutes in temperate climate." FWO Diary Excerpt of August 23-26, 1928. RAC.

123 O'Connor, F.W. "The Teaching of…," op. cit.: 222-224.

greater financial support. The prevention and cure of tropical diseases, he wrote:

> ...requires considerable augmentation of staff for research and teaching as well as much more equipment, all of which cost money. One feels that it will only be a question of time when those high-minded philanthropists who give so much of their substance for the relief of their fellows in the temperate climates will begin to consider more than they have in the past the advisability of contributing towards studies which are of vital concern to the inhabitants of two-thirds of the globe.[124]

An Academic Career

Indeed, these "high-minded philanthropists" were actually paying O'Connor's salary at Columbia. In 1927-28 the General Education Board of the Rockefeller Foundation had given Columbia a grant of $60,000 to create a unit devoted to tropical medicine as part of the Department of Medicine.[125] The monies were to be awarded on a decreasing basis over five years, and it was these funds that covered O'Connor's salary.[126] The not-so-invisible hand of the Rockefeller Foundation also orchestrated two additional moves in an ingenious roundelay of interlocking careers. O'Connor was replaced at the DME

---

124   Ibid.: 224.
125   Annual Report of the General Education Board, Rockefeller Foundation, 1927-1928: 12. RAC.
126   Annual Report of the General Education Board, 1927-28. Rockefeller Foundation, RAC.

by Dr. Robert A. Lambert, who became Pearce's deputy.[127] And the vacancy left by Lambert at the School of Tropical Medicine in Puerto Rico was filled by Dr. Earl B. McKinley, formerly with the RF's International Health Board.[128] The dynamics of the 'old boy network' thus assured everyone a new position (and probably a promotion), while maintaining a salutary equilibrium between the academic and foundation worlds.

On May 28, 1928, the College of Physicians and Surgeons approved O'Connor's appointment as Associate Professor of Medicine at a salary of $8,000.[129] This assured O'Connor a comfortable income and a measure of stability.[130] It also provided him a new audience.

At Columbia, O'Connor was distinguished not only by his area of expertise, but also by his accent, bearing, clothes, and riveting teaching style. Unlike the rest of his colleagues, O'Connor wore morning coat (pinstripe pants and a cutaway jacket) to class. To complete the air of quiet formality, he

---

127 "Appointments," *Rockefeller Foundation Quarterly Bulletin* 1928; 2 (2): 176.

128 Ibid.: 177.

129 It was explicitly stated that his appointment was at "no salary," the full amount "to be provided by the General Education Board," Minutes of the Committee on Administration, College of Physicians and Surgeons, Columbia University. May 28, 1928. Archives and Special Collections, A. C. Long Library, Columbia University, New York, NY.

130 This was the equivalent of $90,000 in current dollars.

carried a bowler hat and an ebony cane.[131] But it was his gift of eloquent speech that most effectively set him apart. In the words of a former student:

> O'Connor quickly proved himself a shameless Gaelic spellbinder. Speaking in a mellifluous, rolling baritone, he eschewed the medical jargon that routinely scrambled our brains and muddled our attempts at recall. When he talked of parasites as creatures of great beauty, there was a touch of poetry in his words. He wasn't so much a medical lecturer as a storyteller, a spinner of parasitological tales that had the effect of etching the little monsters on your mind in a way that made them hard to forget.
>
> [...]
>
> After two years of medical school—two years of lectures so tedious as to be almost life-threatening—O'Connor's class was as exciting as sex...[132]

While many students regarded tropical medicine as esoteric and impractical, some attached themselves to O'Connor "like New Guinea tapeworms," benefiting from his knowledge and enjoying his tales of the years with Manson

---

131   Kean, B.H. *MD*, op.cit.: 18. Attention to dress was of paramount importance to Edwardian gentlemen, and it is likely that, coming of age during that era, O'Connor was socialized into the strict dress code that shaped his later habits. "The Edwardian gentleman...needed a full wardrobe: a tweed suit for the country, frock coat for business, dinner jacket for the evening at home, tail coat for going out, and a series of boots, shirts, cuffs, and waistcoats of different styles to match." Thompson, P. *The Edwardians*, op. cit.: 19.

132   Kean, B.H., *MD*, op.cit.: 18.

and his travels and travails. Over time, O'Connor's sleuthing exploits became "the stuff of legend."[133]

O'Connor's Columbia affiliation allowed him to maintain his ties to Puerto Rico and continue the research that he had begun in 1927. In subsequent visits to the island, he once again collaborated with researchers at the School of Tropical Medicine. Returning to the island in early 1929, he experimented with a new treatment for filariasis that involved a subcutaneous injection of sulphasphenamine[134] and novocaine[135] at the point where patients reported that their pain had started or where it was most intense at the time of recurrence.[136] Some 32 persons were treated, with 20 being reported on. Among the latter, no inflammatory reaction was observed, and 18 had had no recurrence in their condition. Although O'Connor pointed out that it was "too early to speculate on permanency of relief,"[137] he clearly felt that the results warranted publication and consideration by a wider audience. Another clinical report based on his work in Puerto Rico involved the post-mortem histological examination of a victim of filariasis.[138] The findings in this case allowed O'Connor to shed light on both the reason for the confirmed periodicity of filaria, and the mechanisms through which the microfilariae reached the blood vessels of

---

133 Ibid.: 22.

134 An anti-microbial compound.

135 A local anesthetic used on a wide range of nerve blocks.

136 O'Connor, F.W. "An Experiment in the Treatment of Filarial Lymphangitis by Subcutaneous Injection." *Porto Rico Journal of Public Health and Tropical Medicine* 1929; V (1): 11-15.

137 Ibid.: 14.

138 O'Connor, F.W. "Filarial Periodicity, with Observations on the Mechanism of the Migration of the Microfilariae from the Parent Worm to the Blood Stream." *Porto Rico Journal of Public Health and Tropical Medicine* 1931; VI (3): 263-272.

its victim. Concerning the former, his findings strengthened the hypothesis that periodicity was associated with the simultaneous cyclical parturition of the female worm. As to the latter, he concluded that "migration of the microfilariae is a sudden and rapid one with probably a pause, lasting perhaps some hours, in the vessels nearing to the lymphatic through which they have passed."[139]

After publishing his findings from Puerto Rico, O'Connor carried out epidemiological and parasitological research in Antigua.[140] By 1932 he felt confident that he had unlocked at least some of the secrets of filariasis, and was ready to share his findings with the medical community. The opportunity for this arose in May 1932 when he traveled to England to lecture before his former colleagues at the London School of Tropical Medicine and Hygiene and the Royal Society of Tropical Medicine.

For O'Connor, the visit was both a homecoming and a "victory lap" allowing him to compare his work and circumstances with those of his esteemed peers in England. By then, O'Connor had become an American citizen and was comfortably ensconced in the academic culture of Columbia College of Physicians and Surgeons, where he commanded the respect of the faculty and the awe of the students. In contrast, he found that conditions at the London School of Tropical Medicine were "awful, much worse than [he] had ever known them before:" student enrollment was declining, the atmosphere was characterized by uneasiness and lack of cooperation, and

---

139   Ibid.: 268.
140   O'Connor, F.W. "Filariasis in Antigua." *Journal of Tropical Medicine and Hygiene* 1937; 40 (3): 25-31.

the faculty was wracked by internecine fights.[141] Philip Manson-Bahr had inherited Sir Patrick Manson's mantle at the School, and O'Connor found himself the guest of his one-time rival, who was "exceedingly kind and did everything to please [him]." Mrs. Manson-Bahr, however, was not as welcoming. In O'Connor's words:

> ...there is no mistaking the facts that his wife did not and does not want me. She did not shake hands when she met me and cleared out...before I could say goodbye [...] I feel more than anything that she resents my having come to the fore in my particular subject and according to her imagination having somewhat eclipsed her man in this line. All this is thoroughly understood by me and I resent it not at all.[142]

A preliminary meeting with a few other parasitologists was "thrillingly interesting" and added to O'Connor's confidence that he was on the right track concerning the etiology and transmission of filariasis. Indeed, one faculty member felt that O'Connor had "definitely established hyperfilariation and the cause of elephantiasis and also demonstrated the true method by which the microfilaria reach the blood," thereby making "a tremendous contribution to the subject."[143] But the "great day" was the following day, when O'Connor was to formally present his work to a wider and potentially more contentious audience. Years of teaching and lecturing did not quell his nerves, and he feared that the atmosphere would become "very hot."

---

141   Excerpt of Francis W. O'Connor Diary dated May 14, 1932. NYAM.
142   Ibid.
143   Excerpt of Francis W. O'Connor Diary dated May 18, 1921. NYAM.

Still, he expected to emerge with a sense of satisfaction and a vindication of the support he had received from Manson and Pearce, among others.[144] In fact, the presentation was a complete success. In O'Connor's words:

> The meeting was a remarkable experience and beyond my wildest hopes, so much so that now that it is over a severe reaction has set in and I am going through a period of depression [...] There were about 150 people. The demonstration looked magnificent, twenty microscopes with splendid specimens and description of each specimen typed on a card beside each scope. [...] I was not a bit nervous...I was full of fight...I began considering the paper as read and I then started with the lantern. The slides went perfectly. I was told afterwards...that my elocution was good and my enunciation clear and sharp. I was applauded when I finished...all were completely eulogistic [...] Thus none tackled me adversely and the audience was most enthusiastic; I was very much astonished as I certainly expected some opposition.[145]

This professional triumph was followed by a restful and nostalgic trip to Ireland, where he visited friends and relatives and toured the country. Nearing the end of his stay, he ruminated on the culture into which he had been born: "Ireland is a strange place and we Irish are strange people," he wrote. "Even before we were conquered by the Anglo-Normans we were a restless, brooding, and difficult people.

---

144 Excerpt of Diary of Francis W. O'Connor dated May 15, 1932. NYAM.
145 Excerpt of Diary of Francis W. O'Connor dated May 20, 1932. NYAM.

I think that we are better mixed with those who know us not and who are indifferent to our introspective attitude. At the same time the Celtic imagination has its points and is creative. It is sad though here to realize the wonderful possibilities of achievement that will never be realized because sects, groups and even individuals cannot work together for the universal good."[146]

This is likely to have been O'Connor's last visit to Ireland. Returning to New York, he focused on infectious diseases closer to home, participating in the investigation of a deadly disease outbreak which felled many persons visiting the Chicago World's Fair of 1933. Although the fair celebrated a "Century of Progress" and showcased advances in preventive medicine,[147] it would uncover a public health problem that was unrecognized and thus unaddressed. Out-of-town guests became ill with a "mystery plague." Over time, there would be 1,409 cases and 98 deaths scattered throughout 43 states, the territory of Hawaii, and three Canadian provinces.[148] The disease baffled fair officials and local doctors, and O'Connor's interest in the disease was piqued. He went to Chicago, where

---

146   Excerpt of Diary of Francis W. O'Connor dated July 17, 1932. NYAM.

147   One example was the Infant Incubator Exhibit which was installed as part of the fair. There, a total of 70 premature or underweight Chicago babies were kept and cared for during the Exposition. People prominent in the medical and nursing professions had the opportunity to mingle with the infants. Dye, Donald and Tarpey, Karen. "Maternity and Infant Care Services in Chicago Retrospectus: Our Legacy, Our Challenge." In George F. Smith and Dharmapuri Vidyasagar, eds. *Historical Review and Recent Advances in Neonatal and Perinatal Medicine*. Mead Johnson Nutritional Division, 1980.
See: http://www.neonatology.org/classics/mj1980/ch245.html.

148   Jones and Bartlett Public Health Products: http//publicheatlh.jbpub.com/turnock/3e/chapter01.pdf.

he examined a sampling of the victims' stools. He quickly identified the pathogen as *Entamoeba histolytica,* which he and Wenyon had studied extensively in Egypt. The question was: Why had this parasite, which is most often associated with filth and spread by contact with infected feces, spread in a sanitary city such as Chicago? O'Connor went to Chicago and spent the next several weeks doing shoeleather epidemiology. He interviewed victims in the Chicago area and tracked down others across the country, interviewing them by telephone. Food-related questions elicited no consistent pattern. But practically everyone he talked to had stayed at the Congress Hotel in downtown Chicago and the puzzle was quickly solved:

> The answer came to O'Connor in a flash. He rushed to the Congress, descended into the dank basement, and there found exactly what he had been looking for: two rusty pipes. One pipe carried tap water to the guest rooms; the other channeled raw sewage out of the building. Somehow, the pipes had accidentally fused ("a marriage of inconvenience," O'Connor called it) and the hotel's supply of drinking water had become a lusty breeding ground of the deadly amebas. O'Connor had saved the day.[149]

Although the credit for finding the source of the "plague" went to Herman Bundesen, Chicago's long-time Commissioner of Health, O'Connor, convinced that "the uncloaking of amebas [was] reward enough," was satisfied that the culprit had been found.[150]

---

149   Kean, B.H., *MD*, op. cit.: 22.
150   Ibid.

This investigation, however, may have been responsible for O'Connor's death four years later. While the obituary in *The New York Times* merely stated that he had died at Columbia Presbyterian Medical Center following "an operation to relieve an intestinal obstruction,"[151] a more complete account of his death attributed his lethal ailment to the sequelae of his research in Chicago. Whether as a foolhardy caper or a deliberate act of self-experimentation, O'Connor had drunk the contaminated tap water and subsequently suffered from acute amebic dysentery. When he died, two amebic abscesses were found in his liver.[152] He was therefore praised for "the courage of his convictions to which he sacrificed his life."[153]

Whatever the details of his death, there is no doubt that his life was well-lived. The geographic and occupational zigzags that took him to the far side of the world and spurred him to engage in clinical medicine, research, administration, and teaching contributed much to his versatility and persona. While lacking both wealth and health for much of his life, O'Connor had the intellectual curiosity and gentlemanly manners that assured him access to the leading medical minds of his day. He parlayed these advantages into a research career and academic success, mentoring others much as he had been nurtured by McGavin, Manson, Wenyon, Alcock, and Ross.

Always reflective, O'Connor took stock of his life in a letter written one year before he died. In a statement that was read at his memorial service, he wrote as follows:

---

151   "Dr. F. W. O'Connor, Columbia Teacher." *The New York Times* October 4, 1937: 21.

152   Manson-Bahr, P. *History of the School of Tropical Medicine*, op. cit.: 189.

153   Ibid.

Life is all a matter of compensation. For happiness we must have sadness, with success we must have failure; for idealism, disillusion; for friendship, enmity. Realizing this I have no reason to complain. I've had much happiness, great friends, and some success. My misery, enemies, and failures have made me appreciate the former. But above all I have had what so few people experience, namely, a very interesting life with hardly a moment of monotony. This, you will agree, is a proud statement for a man who has lived fifty-three years in the vortex of the world's activities.[154]

---

154 Excerpt of letter from Francis W. O'Connor to Madge Cook, dated ca. September 20, 1937, accompanying letter from Constance R. Hulse, Columbia University College of Physicians and Surgeons, to Dr. Archibald Malloch, New York Academy of Medicine. February 23, 1939. Papers of Francis W. O'Connor, NYAM.

The Apogee of Tropical Medicine:

3

An Epidemiologic Portrait of Puerto Rico in 1927

José G. Rigau-Pérez

F rancis O'Connor's diary of his visit to Puerto Rico in 1927 provides a first-hand account of how the island looked and functioned. The diary also describes the people, as well as their poor health and the efforts to improve it. Most histories of the period focus on the economic conditions, leading up to the devastation produced by Hurricane San Felipe (13 September 1928). In a contrasting image of optimism and relative success, O'Connor shows what had been achieved before the hurricane hit, and the persons and policies that made that progress possible.

The changes that have occurred in Puerto Rico and the world since O'Connor's time may limit the understanding of current readers of his diary, especially if they are not familiar with the diagnoses and concepts that were basic to the diarist's profession. The panorama of diseases that O'Connor describes in his diary is portrayed by Puerto Rican surrealist painter Julio Tomás Martínez (1878-1954), in a large canvas titled *Los vicios* (The Vices, see next page). This depicts a

Los Vicios, Julio Tomás Martínez (1878-1954), Colección René Vélez Marichal. Foto: Johnny Betancourt

multitude of evil forces attacking the population of Puerto Rico, such as giant mosquitoes, tuberculosis, syphilis, and cancer, surrounding a parade of floats that allude to capitalist exploitation, alcoholism, gambling, and prostitution.[1] Just as the painting requires the explanation of its symbols, O'Connor's diary requires an explanation of the context and the technical language it contains. Two major components of this analysis, the diseases and the institutions, were undergoing radical transformations in 1927. What people knew and thought of them at the time is not necessarily what we know and think about them now. This essay therefore examines the burden of illness and mortality in Puerto Rico in 1927 and provides a historical summary of the social impact and the public response to these threats.

A sugar-based economy

O'Connor was witness to a singular moment in the history of public health and medical institutions in Puerto Rico. Most of the Puerto Rican physicians with whom he interacted were recent graduates of United States medical schools, and developed distinguished careers as researchers, clinicians, and public health officials.[2] New facilities were being inaugurated to provide up-to-date treatment for patients with leprosy, mental illness, and tuberculosis, and preventive services to the presumably healthy population. The Tuberculosis Sanatorium even served as an attractive

---

1   Nolla, Olga. "El simbolismo criollo de Julio Tomás Martínez." *Cupey* (Revista de la Universidad Metropolitana de Puerto Rico) 1990; 7 (1-2): 4-16.

2   Arana-Soto, Salvador. *Catálogo de médicos de P.R. de siglos pasados (con muchos de éste)*. San Juan: n.p., 1966.

venue for O'Connor's farewell champagne dinner.[3] These medical buildings were visible proof of improved care made accessible to the population, but also reflected the poor state of health on the island, as will be described below. All the medical research and public health effort were necessary to counteract the consequences of an economy based primarily on one product: cane sugar.

Between 1900 and 1940 sugarcane cultivation was the island's main economic activity. In 1928, sugar accounted for 53% of the value of Puerto Rico's exports, followed by tobacco and cigars, which accounted for 20%.[4] In this corporate plantation economy, the cultivation of food staples, which had decreased markedly in the previous century, was almost abandoned.[5] Most of the population of Puerto Rico lived in rural areas. Unemployment was high (over 12% for males), but even among the employed, work was mostly seasonal, so thousands had no stable source of income.[6] Investors in sugarcane corporations earned handsome dividends (the three largest corporations in Puerto Rico paid an average annual dividend of 26% from 1920 to 1929).[7] At the same time, laborers earned less than subsistence wages. A study commissioned by the Legislative Assembly found that in 1930 a family of three needed a minimal income of

---

3   O'Connor. *Diary...* (November 15).

4   Dietz, James L. *Historia económica de Puerto Rico*. San Juan: Huracán, 1989: 118.

5   Ayala, César. *American Sugar Kingdom*. Chapel Hill, NC: University of North Carolina Press, 1999: 164.

6   Dietz, J.L. *Historia económica*, op.cit.: 149.

7   Bird, Esteban A. *A report on the sugar industry in relation to the social and economic system of Puerto Rico*. San Juan: Bureau of Supplies, Printing and Transportation, 1941: 39-41; 129.

$1,142 for survival, but laborers (whose families were rarely that small) earned only $320 to $720 per year.[8] Women tried to supplement the family finances by sewing or embroidery at home. Some of O'Connor's acquaintances on board the ship sailing to San Juan mentioned the needlework industry, but failed to comment on how poorly it paid—2 cents an hour or less for most needle workers in the 1930s.[9]

Sugar was an extraordinarily lucrative product in Puerto Rico because of two conditions that were absent in neighboring islands—abundance of unemployed workers, and tariff-free access to United States markets.[10] The intensity of sugarcane cultivation in Puerto Rico is shown by the tonnage of sugar produced per square mile of territory, which in 1930 was 22 in the Dominican Republic, 122 in Cuba, and 246 in Puerto Rico, by far the smallest of the three countries.[11] Raw sugar prices (and workers' salaries) increased during World War I but fell markedly in 1920, from 20 cents to 4.5 cents per pound, with the recovery of European beet crops.[12] Three disasters in quick succession (hurricane San Felipe, 1928; the stock market crash, 1929; and hurricane San Ciprián, 1932) produced further decreases in

8   Silvestrini, Blanca G. and Luque de Sánchez, María Dolores. *Historia de Puerto Rico: trayectoria de un pueblo*. San Juan: Cultural Puertorriqueña, 1987: 468. For a personal account of the life of a laborer's family, see Justiniano, Carmen Luisa. *Con valor y a como dé lugar: memorias de una jíbara puertorriqueña*. Río Piedras, P.R.: Editorial de la Universidad de Puerto Rico, 1994.

9   Silvestrini, B.G. and Luque de Sánchez, M.D. *Historia de Puerto Rico*, op.cit.: 444.

10   Ayala, C. *American Sugar*, op.cit.: 166, 173, 180, 225.

11   Costa, Marithelma. "Introducción." In Enrique Laguerre. *La llamarada*. San Juan: Plaza Mayor, 2002: 9-41; using data from Ayala, C. *American Sugar*, op.cit: 70.

12   Ayala, ibid.: 71, 87, 97.

salaries and concomitant increases in food prices.[13] The local party realignments and unstable social peace of the 1920s exploded in the 1930s in a succession of strikes, political assassinations, police massacres of unarmed protestors, and a level of general violence that raised the homicide rate from less than 10 per 100,000 population in the 1920s to about 18 per 100,000 population in 1935, a level that was not seen again until 1974.[14]

Public health infrastructure in Puerto Rico

The Puerto Rico Department of Health was created in 1912, but it evolved over the next 20 years in response to legislation, emerging problems, available funding, and the priorities of the different Commissioners of Health.[15] Most municipalities provided (or meant to provide) charity medical care to indigent patients through hospitals or public-assistance physicians. The relatively small number of physicians (331 in 1927, or one per 4,500 persons), the limited finances of most cities, and the dispersed rural habitation of most of the

---

13   Costa, M. "Introducción," op. cit.: 33.
14   Departamento de Salud de Puerto Rico. *Informe anual de estadísticas vitales 1977.* San Juan: Departamento de Salud, n.d.: 75; and Ayala, C. *American Sugar*, op.cit: 237-238. A family anecdote may be more eloquent than statistics. My great-aunt Virginia Vélez, an elementary ("Normal") school teacher, wife of a physician, and one of the first women in Puerto Rico to be issued a driver's license, was also a political activist in the 1930s. She drove women voters from rural areas in Guánica to their assigned voting locations, but because of the tensions of the times, "just in case," she carried a gun in the car's glove compartment—she never had to use it.
15   Costa Mandry, Oscar. *Apuntes para la historia de la medicina en Puerto Rico.* San Juan, P. R.; Departamento de Salud (mimeographed), 1971: 123-133.

population meant that medical care was often not available.[16] Antibiotics had not yet been developed, federal government assistance for the poorest did not materialize until the 1930s, and economic development had aggravated living conditions for the working class.

The battle against anemia caused by intestinal worms (uncinariasis) was emblematic of the medical research and public health efforts in Puerto Rico in the first half of the twentieth century. In 1899, Dr. Bailey K. Ashford identified hookworm as the cause of a lethal anemia among displaced rural residents. Over the decades, he exercised considerable influence as researcher, clinician, U.S. Army medical officer, unofficial advisor of American governors, and popular figure in local society in obtaining insular government funding for public health and medical research. First, the Anemia Commission (1904) led to the establishment of treatment clinics in every municipality, then the Institute of Tropical Medicine (1913) conducted research and training on the problems of rural areas, and later the School of Tropical Medicine (1926), in collaboration with Columbia University, brought outside investigators to work on the health problems of Puerto Rico.[17]

With the island's economic and sanitary state, no matter how hard the Department of Health pursued modernization, it was oppressively burdened with the need to provide what could only amount to relief. It was difficult to find resources for preventive public health (immunization, education, environmental monitoring, and enforcement)

---

16   Costa Mandry, O. *Apuntes*, op.cit.: 23.
17   Fernós, Rodrigo. "The social factors affecting the diffusion of parasitology to Puerto Rico and Hong Kong." *PR Health Sci J* 2001; 20: 367-375.

when there was such a constant outcry for diagnostic and treatment services. For almost two decades after O'Connor's visit to Puerto Rico, the United States government did not have an agency that would provide such assistance to states. From 1898 to 1917, when the government of Puerto Rico was even more closely controlled from Washington, DC than in 1927, the U.S. Public Health Service had detailed its officers to assist in local public health matters as it did, for example, in 1923, for the evaluation of the tuberculosis problem.[18]

Nevertheless, in 1926 the Puerto Rico Department of Health established new administrative and service structures for its prevention activities, chief among them a Division of Epidemiology to analyze disease surveillance data, and to organize two Public Health Units (in Río Piedras, a city later to become a suburb of San Juan, and Yabucoa, in the southeast sector of the island).[19] These Units were supported by funding and technical assistance from the Rockefeller Foundation (O'Connor's employer). They sought to extend the work of the Department's programs to the municipal level by coordinating local activities such as sanitary and school inspection, food safety, prenatal and child welfare,

18   Rigau-Pérez, J.G. "La salud en Puerto Rico en el siglo XX." *PR Health Sci J* 2000; 19: 357-368.

19   Anonymous [possibly Eduardo Garrido Morales]. "Report of the Division of Epidemiology of the Department of Health, 1926-1927." *PR Journal of Public Health and Tropical Medicine* 1927-1928; 3: 113-115 [repeated 422-424]; and Commissioner of Health of Porto Rico. *Report of the Commissioner of Health of Porto Rico to the Governor of Porto Rico for the Fiscal Year ending June 30, 1927.* San Juan: Bureau of Supplies, Printing, and Transportation, 1929: 17-38.

tuberculosis and sexually transmitted diseases clinics, and related services. Their success was so remarkable that by 1938 every municipality was covered by a public health unit.[20]

The Rockefeller Foundation in Puerto Rico

As historian John Farley indicates, before the establishment of the World Health Organization in 1948, the Rockefeller Foundation was arguably the world's most important agency for public health work.[21] Since 1919, the Foundation provided expert assistance and funds to the Puerto Rico Department of Health in its campaigns against hookworm, malaria, and plague. The Foundation also provided scholarships to train public health officials and supported the creation of Public Health Units. Either "la Rockefeller" had assigned staff or funds for a particular disease project, or officials had received specialized training through a Foundation scholarship, or its officials in Puerto Rico served as on-site investigators for their laboratory

20   Ramírez de Arellano, Annette B. "The politics of public health in Puerto Rico: 1926-1940." *Revista de Salud Pública de Puerto Rico* 1981; 3: 35-58. For a recent paean to the work of public health nurses in this period, see Magali García Ramis's novel, *Las horas del sur*. San Juan: Callejón, 2005: 231.
21   Farley, John. *To cast out disease: a history of the International Health Division of the Rockefeller Foundation (1913-1951)*. New York: Oxford University Press, 2004: 2.

counterparts in New York.[22] Therefore, the assistance provided by the Foundation touched all activities of the Department of Health. In 1908, Wickliffe Rose, the first Director of the Rockefeller Sanitary Commission, examined Ashford's activities on site, before instituting the hookworm campaigns in the southern United States.[23] Those campaigns in turn led to the development of county health units in the states, and in the 1920s it was the Foundation that was guiding the establishment of public health units, public health nursing, and hookworm eradication on the island.[24]

O'Connor and his point of view

The political conflicts of colonial situations must have been familiar to O'Connor, born and raised in Ireland during English rule. He was a middle class colonial subject (by birth, accent, and religious upbringing) identified with the colonizers (by education, citizenship, and military service) but who affirmed "the potentiality of scientists...to

---

22   In 1934, Drs. W.C. Earle and W.A. Sawyer sent sputum specimens from patients of an influenza epidemic in Puerto Rico to Dr. Thomas Francis, Jr. at the Hospital of the Rockefeller Institute. Francis obtained the first influenza virus isolated in America (identified as A/PR/34/H0N1), used in early vaccines and as a reference strain for laboratory tests. Francis, Jr, Thomas. "Transmission of influenza by a filterable virus." *Science* 1934; 80: 457-459. Costa Mandry underscores the assistance provided by Dr. Juan Arruza, of the Department of Health's Biological Laboratory; see Costa Mandry, O. *Apuntes*, op.cit.: 134.

23   Ashford, Bailey K. *A soldier in science.* New York: William Morrow and Co., 1934 (Facsimilar edition, San Juan: Editorial de la Universidad de Puerto Rico, 1998): 96-98.

24   Ramírez de Arellano, A.B. "The politics...," op. cit; and Farley, J. *Rockefeller*, op.cit.: 31-37.

smash nationalism".[25] He contrasted the "genuinely good spirit in which the Spanish and American doctors mix and cooperate" with "the clearly bad feeling which exists outside the profession between Porto Ricans and what they designate their U.S. 'masters,'" ascribing the handicaps to worldwide "political agents" and "uneducated and ill-bred tourists" while failing to recognize the intricacies and peculiarities of these social relations within a dependent political situation.[26]

O'Connor recognizes, as the first item of his "Summary of Impressions," that Puerto Ricans were "exploited by absentee landlords who leave no chances for the small producer,"[27] but he manifests an unexpected political *naiveté* when he identifies poverty, disease, ignorance, and superstition as the causes that left Puerto Ricans prey to that exploitation. In the United States, the antitrust laws at the beginning of the twentieth century, passed because of the generalized outrage of a society capable of legal and political action, managed to curtail only the more egregious abuses of big business.[28] O'Connor's recognition of primordial economic and social determinants of health may nevertheless distinguish his views from those of his colleagues at the Rockefeller Foundation. Most of them held to a very narrow model of public health action in which disease was seen as a

25   In 1926, Sinclair Lewis had won a Pulitzer Prize for his novel *Arrowsmith*, which described the career of an ambitious young scientist, Martin Arrowsmith, who joins the McGurk Institute (a thin disguise for the Rockefeller Institute) and investigates a plague epidemic on a Caribbean island. The novel underscores the contrast between the promises of scientific research and the psychological and social forces that surround it. It is very likely that O'Connor was aware of the novel's publication and subject.

26   O'Connor. *Diary...* (October 31).

27   O'Connor. *Diary...* (November 21).

28   Ayala, C. *American Sugar*, op.cit.: 47.

cause of poverty, so that any effort to cure or prevent a malady would promote the well-being of the weakest members of the community.[29] The arguments against such limited focus were clearly voiced even in O'Connor's time, and by the very researchers he met in Puerto Rico.[30]

Not intended for public view, O'Connor's diary is written in a personal engaging tone that occasionally turns into the voice of a member of the ruling class. In contrast to his expressed pity for the indigent sick in La Perla, a slum outside the walls of San Juan, he refers to them as "the poor brutes".[31] The next day he writes of the "revolting appearance" and "foolish" love letters of lepers. He correctly states that "leprosy often sterilizes the males,"[32] but it is his unfounded opinion that "it has the opposite effect with the women."[33] When he wonders—or repeats a remark—about the academic inferiority of male students at the University of Puerto Rico, which "may be due to [the] nature of sex life,"[34] he echoes the connection between masculinity and domination in imperialist discourse and the old fear of colonial administrators that life in the tropics (and especially

---

29   Farley, J. *Rockefeller*, op.cit.: 118, 123, 124, 244, 285, 294, 296.

30   See for example: Fernós Isern, Antonio. "Death rates in Porto Rico and some other countries." *PR Journal of Public Health and Tropical Medicine* 1928; 4: 70-77; and Suárez, Ramón M. "Puerto Rico and some of its health problems." *Bol Asoc Med P Rico* 1930; 22 (181): 197-200.

31   O'Connor. *Diary...* (November 11).

32   Britton, Warwick J. and Lockwood, Diana N.J. "Leprosy." *Lancet* 2004; 363: 1209-1219.

33   A much more sympathetic portrayal of female lepers is given by Spanish writer Eduardo Zamacois in his account of a visit to Isla de Cabras in 1917. *La alegría de andar*. Madrid: Renacimiento, 1920: 129-134.

34   O'Connor. *Diary...*(November 8).

what was considered excessive sexual stimulation) leads to the decline of man's physical and intellectual vigor.[35] But perhaps O'Connor was reflecting the prevailing views of university administrators: in one of Emilio Belaval's contemporary short stories on university life, the physician who examines a freshman finds him too thin and immediately advises against "too much sex, too much thinking."[36]

Tropical medicine

The decade around O'Connor's visit marked the apogee of the discipline of tropical medicine in Puerto Rico. Years before, the specialty's founders astonished the world by the demonstration of the cause of malaria (Laveran in Algeria, 1880), the implication of mosquitoes as vectors of disease (Manson for filaria in China, 1877; Ross for malaria in India, 1897; Finlay and Reed for yellow fever in Cuba, 1900) and many other discoveries. This knowledge was used by the colonial powers to protect their military and subject (labor) populations. The disease classification of "tropical diseases" grew out of the colonial expansion of European nations and the United States at the end of the nineteenth century.[37] The term served as a convenient catchall to refer to diseases usually

---

35   Anderson, Warwick. "The trespass speaks: white masculinity and colonial breakdown." *American Historical Review* 1997; 102: 1343-1370; and Hoganson, Kristin L. *Fighting for American manhood: how gender politics provoked the Spanish-American and Philippine-American wars.* New Haven: Yale University Press, 1998.
36   Belaval, Emilio S. *Los cuentos de la universidad (1923-1929).* Barcelona: Rumbos, 1967: 11.
37   Worboys, M. "The emergence and early development of parasitology." In K.S. Warren and J.Z. Bowers, eds. *Parasitology: A Global Perspective.* New York: Springer-Verlag, 1983: 1-18.

transmitted only within certain boundaries of geography and climate.[38] Historians have noted that the public health priorities of colonial administrations did not necessarily coincide with the most pressing needs of native communities.[39] Even in O'Connor's time, the "tropical" label was criticized. Both Dr. Pedro Ortiz, the Commissioner of Health in Puerto Rico, and Dr. Antonio Fernós, the Assistant Commissioner, were among the critics.[40] "Tropical medicine" never defined the health concerns or practices in tropical areas, because the largest proportion of diseases found in those countries was and still is not due to parasites or vector-borne agents, but to globally distributed causes such as tuberculosis, bacterial infections, and at present HIV and smoking, whose prevalence and severity are increased by the conjunction of poverty, hunger, and lack of medical care.[41] O'Connor's account is focused on his interests as an educator and parasitologist, although the principal health concerns of Puerto Rico at the time were not limited to parasitic diseases.

---

38   Arnold, D. "The place of 'the tropics' in Western medical ideas since 1750." *Trop Med Intl Hlth* 1997; 2: 303-313.

39   Silvestrini, Blanca G. "La política de salud pública de los Estados Unidos en Puerto Rico, 1898-1913: Consecuencias en el proceso de americanización." In Blanca G. Silvestrini, ed. *Politics, society and culture in the Caribbean. Selected papers of the XIV Conference of Caribbean Historians.* San Juan: Association of Caribbean Historians and Universidad de Puerto Rico, 1983: 67-83; Farley, John. *Bilharzia: A History of Imperial Tropical Medicine.* New York, N.Y.: Cambridge University Press, 1991: 5-10, 99-100; and Manderson, Lenore. "Public health developments in colonial Malaya: colonialism and the politics of prevention." *Am J Public Health* 1999; 89: 102-107.

40   Ortiz, Pedro N. "The tropics from the public-health standpoint: legends and facts." *Porto Rico Health Review* 1927; 2(12): 3-13; and Fernós Isern, Antonio. "The White–and the Tropics. *Porto Rico Health Review* 1926; 2 (2): 6-7.

41   Warren, Kenneth S. "Tropical medicine or tropical health: the Heath Clark Lectures, 1988." *Rev Infect Dis* 1990; 12: 142-156; and Farmer, P.E. *Infections and Inequalities: The Modern Plagues.* Berkeley, CA: University of California Press, 2001.

The burden of disease

To examine the most important diseases in 1927, we must consider their impact on mortality as well as their effect on the population's general wellbeing. Among all diseases with a primary locus of transmission in tropical areas, the most calamitous for mankind are four transmitted by the bite of a mosquito;[42] four transmitted by other arthropods;[43] two acquired by contact with a contaminated environment: soil (intestinal nematode—roundworm—infections) or water with infected snails (schistosomiasis); one acquired through contact with contaminated secretions or by flies (trachoma);[44] and leprosy, for which close, prolonged personal contact is the suspected mode of transmission. Of this list, the major producer of days of illness and early deaths is by far malaria, followed distantly by filariasis, leishmaniasis, and intestinal nematodes.[45] Of these global scourges, Japanese encephalitis and the four infections transmitted by arthropods other than mosquitoes have never been documented in Puerto Rico.

The 14 most common causes of death in Puerto Rico in 1927 are listed in the table below, in the diagnostic

---

42 Malaria, dengue hemorrhagic fever, Japanese encephalitis, and lymphatic filariasis.

43 Onchocerciasis, trypanosomiasis, Chagas' disease, and leishmaniasis. An arthropod is an individual of the phylum Arthropoda, which is the largest phylum of animals, such as arachnids, crustaceans, and insects, many species of which are parasites or are vectors of disease-causing organisms (*Dorland's Pocket;* op. cit.: 75).

44 Trachoma is a contagious disease of the conjunctiva and cornea. (*Dorland's Pocket;* op. cit.: 688)

45 Murray, C.J.L. and Lopez A.D., eds. *The Global Burden of Disease: A Comprehensive Assessment of Mortality and Disability from Diseases, Injuries, and Risk Factors in 1990 and Projected to 2020.* Vol. 1. Boston, MA; Harvard School of Public Health, World Health Organization, and World Bank, 1996: 120, 541-576.

terms of the period.[46] It must be emphasized, though, that the true illness burden was undoubtedly underestimated, due to the lack of local resources for diagnosis and data collection.

The table's content suggests two main conclusions: infectious diseases predominate among all causes of death, and some of the causes lack precision. Terms such as nephritis, congenital disability, and senility conceal a variety of conditions and remind us that most patients had no access to microbiologic, radiological, or pathologic diagnosis. If we eliminate these categories and add together the deaths due to tuberculosis, bronchopneumonia, pneumonia, and bronchitis, we are left with a list in which the first cause of death is pulmonary infections. Tuberculosis was the cause of a sizeable portion of the deaths, but, without antibiotics, bacterial pneumonia was also a formidable threat to life.[47]

---

46   Pérez, M.A. "Annual report of the Bureau of Vital Statistics [Porto Rico Health Department, for the year ended December 31, 1930]". *Bol Asoc Med P Rico* 1931; 23 (195): 453-462. Pérez, as Chief of the Bureau of Vital Statistics, received a fellowship from the Rockefeller Foundation's International Health Board for a year of study (1929-1930) at the Johns Hopkins University School of Hygiene and Public Health and to visit the statistics offices of three states and the Metropolitan Life Insurance Company. On return to Puerto Rico he recommended a new law for registration of vital events (Act 24, approved 22 April 1931), reorganized the Bureau, and reanalyzed, by calendar year, the vital data which had previously been reported by fiscal year.

47   O'Connor's comment (October 31) on the scarcity of cases of pneumococcal pneumonia reflects the lack of laboratories and the difficulty in obtaining a specific bacteriologic diagnosis of *Streptococcus pneumoniae* rather than a true absence of the infections (Benítez, C. and Morales Otero, P. "Notes on the biology of pneumococci isolated in Puerto Rico." *PR Journal of Public Health and Tropical Medicine* 1940: 252-262). In contrast, his appreciation (October 31) that there was little rheumatism or valvular disease, that is, damage to the heart muscle or heart valves as a consequence of throat or other infection with a specific type of *Streptococcus* bacteriae, is well documented in the medical literature on Puerto Rico (e.g., Suárez, R.M. "Puerto Rico and some of its health problems...," op. cit.:, 200.)

Cause of death	Deaths	Rate per 100,000 population
Diarrhea and enteritis, all ages	6,000	405.7
Tuberculosis, all forms	3,734	252.6
Nephritis (acute and chronic)	2,310	156.2
Malaria	1,910	129.2
Senility	1,420	96.0
Congenital disability	1,410	95.4
Bronchopneumonia	1,375	93.0
Diseases of the Heart	1,358	91.9
Bronchitis (all forms)	1,164	78.7
Pneumonia (all forms)	1,019	68.9
External causes, all	731	49.4
Uncinariasis	623	42.1
Cancer, all forms	576	39.0
Tetanus	548	37.0
All causes	30,500	2,060.8

The second most common cause of death (diarrhea and enteritis) had a particular impact on small children: the mortality rate from this cause for those less than two years of age was almost 10 times the rate for the population as a whole.[48] Pulmonary infections and diarrhea and enteritis accounted for nearly half of all deaths. Malaria followed, producing almost more casualties than heart disease and

---

48   The rate in Manuel A. Pérez, "Annual Report...", op. cit., is mistaken, calculated using the total population as denominator. I have estimated the number of children under age 2 years for the age-specific rate's correct denominator.

cancer combined. In 1927, with almost as many deaths from tetanus (548) as from cancer (576), the public health situation was radically different from what we now have.

The force with which these infections were affecting the health of the population is reflected in three common health indices: the overall or general mortality, the infant mortality, and the life expectancy at birth.[49] When O'Connor visited Puerto Rico, the overall mortality was 20.6 per thousand population, that is, about 2% of the population died every year (30,500 deaths in an estimated population of about 1,480,000). Infant mortality was 151 per thousand live births, so that about one out of seven infants died before the first birthday. Life expectancy at birth was under 40 years, that is, a person born in 1927 could be expected to die, on average, before age 40 years, if current mortality rates continued to apply.[50] These figures, and what we know of the causes of death operating at the time are typical of populations that have not undergone the so-called "epidemiologic transition" because they have not received the benefits of adequate food, housing, and education, and also of sanitation, public health, and medical measures (such as safe potable water and waste disposal, vaccinations, antibiotics, and hospital care).[51] Similar conditions were found in Europe in the nineteenth century,

---

49   Last, John M. ed. *A Dictionary of Epidemiology*, 3rd ed. New York: Oxford University Press, 1995: 43, 85, 59.

50   Pérez M.A., "Annual Report...," op. cit; and Costa Mandry, O. *Apuntes*, op.cit.: 106. The corresponding vital statistics for Puerto Rico for 2001 are an overall mortality of 7.5 and infant mortality of 9.2 per thousand, and life expectancy at birth of 76 years. Departamento de Salud de Puerto Rico. *Informe anual de estadísticas vitales, 2001*. San Juan: Departamento de Salud, 2003: 167.

51   Omran, Abdel M. "The epidemiologic transition: a theory of the epidemiology of population change." *Milbank Memorial Fund Quarterly* 1971; 49 (4): 509-538.

and Puerto Rico's indicators for 1927 are worse than those found today in the poorest countries of the world.[52]

How did Puerto Rico fare in comparison to the United States? Life expectancy for whites in the United States in 1930 was 70 years (48.5 for African Americans); infant mortality was 60.1 per thousand for whites and 99.9 for African Americans.[53] No category of cause of death in the United States approximated the magnitude of the mortality rates in Puerto Rico. All infectious diseases considered together produced a mortality of 154.7 deaths per 100,000 population in the United States, less than half of the rate registered in Puerto Rico for diarrhea and enteritis (405.7). The 1927 mortality rates in the states of Florida and Louisiana (near the tropics), New York (the residence of the Rockefeller scientists who came as consultants), and Washington, DC, gave further evidence that the "tropical" designation had little to do with estimated risk of death. The overall mortality rate was 12.3 per thousand for Louisiana, New York state, and Washington DC, and 13.3 for Florida, considerably lower than in Puerto Rico, but the rates for "urban colored" citizens, perhaps the more comparable group to Puerto Ricans (using a racial designation as a crude indicator of income and living conditions), were actually the same or higher than on the island (Florida 20.4, Washington, DC 20.5, New York state

---

52   Sachs, Jeffrey D. *The End of Poverty*. New York: Penguin, 2005: 204, 267; and Pan American Health Organization, Area of Health Analysis and Information Systems (AIS). Health Situation in the Americas: Basic Indicators 2004. Washington, DC; 2004: http://www.paho.org/english/dd/ais/BI-brochure2004.pdf (accessed 26 July 2005).

53   Haines, Michael. "Fertility and mortality in the United States." EH.Net Encyclopedia, edited by Robert Whaples. January 22, 2005. URL: http://www.eh.net/encyclopedia/?article=haines.demography (accessed 6 September 2005).

27.3, and Louisiana 27.5 per thousand).[54] According to an analysis of the island's situation conducted in 1928-1929 by the Brookings Institution, "the impoverished state of the masses is in no small measure responsible for the prevalence of disease."[55]   A strong underlying reason for the high rates of death in Puerto Rico was malnutrition. This was well known before O'Connor's visit. The medical examination of Puerto Rican draftees in 1917 and 1918, when the United States mobilized its armed forces to enter World War I, revealed "the pathologic world" of young Puerto Rican males, marked by diseases and chronic malnutrition.[56] Published figures for the first call of draftees (July 5, 1917) indicate a rejection rate of 30 per cent (16,367 rejections out of 55,299 examined men, aged 21 to 30 years). An examining physician summed up the population's condition as "physiologically stripped naked."[57]

Unfortunately the World War I draft information was never used to identify the most common health problems or the population groups at greater risk, so as to guide public

---

54   Bureau of the Census, US Department of Commerce. *Mortality statistics 1927.* Washington, DC: Government Printing Office, 1929: 2-5,19-21: http://www.cdc. gov/nchs/data/vsushistorical/mortstatsh_1927.pdf (accessed 4 September 2005). Infant mortality rates are not included in the report.

55   Clark, Victor S. *Porto Rico and its Problems.* Washington, D.C.: The Brookings Institution, 1930: 55. For a microanalysis at the municipal level, see Echevarría Echevarría, Evelyn. *La muerte nuestra de cada día: pobreza y mortandad en Aguada, 1912-1942.* Master's thesis, Humanities Faculty, University of Puerto Rico, Río Piedras, 1988.

56   Martínez-Álvarez, Antonio. *El tiempo y yo.* San Juan: Editorial Universidad de Puerto Rico, 1972: 310.

57   Ibid., quoting Dr. Salvador Giuliani: "Estamos desnudos fisiológicamente."

health policy in Puerto Rico.[58] A study of the reasons for the high incidence of tuberculosis in Puerto Rico, conducted by Dr. James G. Townsend of the U.S. Public Health Service and published in 1923, documented with statistics and photographs the living conditions of the working and unemployed classes. Townsend did not have access to the World War I draft data, but used the results of examinations of the 1,013 applicants for the U.S. Army in 1921-1923. The majority (618 or 61%) were rejected, and 237 (38%) of those rejected were underweight.[59] He also reported that the 65th Infantry (Puerto Rico) Regiment conducted an "experiment" increasing the Army rations to 5,000 calories per day in 1921, and claimed to have reduced its hospitalization rate to one fourth (from 1,265 hospitalizations per thousand soldiers in 1920 to 319 in 1922).[60]

The examination of 3,006 San Juan schoolchildren (ages 5 to 14 years) in 1921 and 1922 similarly showed poor development (1,902, 63%, were underweight) and so many concurrent diseases that 2,625 (87%) were considered to need some kind of treatment.[61] Even in 1927, 23% of University

---

58   Morales Otero, Pablo and Pérez, Manuel A. "Health and socio-economic studies in Puerto Rico. IV. Physical impairments of adult life among agricultural workers." *PR Journal of Public Health and Tropical Medicine* 1940; 15: 285-313.

59   Townsend, James G. *Tuberculosis survey of the island of Puerto Rico*. Washington, D. C.: U.S. Public Health Service, Public Health Bulletin no. 138, December 1923: 28.

60   Ibid., 44.

61   Fernós Isern, Antonio. "Anotaciones y observaciones derivadas del examen físico de tres millares de niños de escuela puertorriqueños (I)." *Bol Asoc Med P Rico* 1923; 17 (143): 77-86.

of Puerto Rico students were underweight by 15-45 pounds.[62] Two of the first faculty members O'Connor met at the School of Tropical Medicine in San Juan (October 31), Donald H. Cook and Trinidad Rivera, were concerned with evaluating the diet of laborers in Puerto Rico. Using data from their studies (and those of others) Henry C. Sherman, a visiting professor from the Department of Chemistry at Columbia, later concluded that "the inadequate and imbalanced food supply of the majority of Porto Rican families…is perhaps the most serious of predisposing causes of tuberculosis."[63] Unfortunately, not only was the quantity of food insufficient; its quality was poor, and there was little supply of good quality potable water for most of the population.[64]

Important Diseases in Puerto Rico in 1927 and in O'Connor's diary

Some diseases, because of their importance for the population of Puerto Rico and for O'Connor, deserve extended comment. Below I summarize and simplify the natural history and treatment for these conditions.[65] In many of them, treatment to cure the infection (if available) may

---

62   "El peso del 23 por ciento de los estudiantes de nuestra Universidad no es normal. Así lo hizo constar el doctor Saliva en conferencia que dictara." San Juan: *El Mundo*, 11 October 1927: 7.

63   Sherman, Henry C. "A glimpse of social economics in Porto Rico." *PR Journal of Public Health and Tropical Medicine* 1930-1931; 6: 221-228.

64   Clark, V.S. *Porto Rico*, op. cit.: 60-62. Milk was largely unpasteurized (see Note 424). Ponce, one of the largest and most progressive cities, had just begun chlorinating its potable water by 1927. See controversy in *El Mundo*, 27 October 1927: 7, and 28 October 1927: 6, 8, 11.

65   Heymann, D.L. ed. *Control of Communicable Diseases Manual*, 18th. ed. Washington, DC: American Public Health Association, 2004.

only partially reverse the long-term disability. Their history in the world and the Americas, and in Puerto Rico in previous centuries can be found elsewhere.[66] Because the process of disease emergence and control in Puerto Rico has rarely been subjected to historical analysis, I have also suggested links to other contemporary problems in Puerto Rico, and postulated similarities and differences with other locations.

Diseases transmitted from person-to-person

Tuberculosis was until recently a major cause of disability and death throughout the world, and is still a serious threat to health in most of the globe. Its high and widespread incidence, long duration, and dramatic symptoms have had noticeable impact on human survival, politics, and art throughout history.[67] In 1922, the Governor of Puerto Rico asked the Surgeon General of the U.S. Public Health Service to assign an officer to conduct a survey to determine the number and distribution of active cases of tuberculosis on the island, the factors responsible for the spread of disease, and the most practical means of

66   Kiple, Kenneth F. ed. *The Cambridge World History of Human Disease.* New York: Cambridge University Press, 1993; Guerra, Francisco. *Epidemiología americana y filipina 1492-1898.* Madrid: Ministerio de Sanidad y Consumo, 1999; Abbad y Lasierra, Iñigo. *Historia geográfica, civil y natural de la isla de San Juan Bautista de Puerto Rico.* Anotada por José Julián Acosta y Calvo. Estudio introductorio por Gervasio L. García. Madrid: Doce Calles, 2002; Dumont, Enrique. *Ensayo de una historia médico-quirúrgica de la Isla de Puerto Rico,* 2 vols. La Habana: La Antillana, 1875-1876; Del Valle, Francisco. *El campesino puertorriqueño.* Puerto Rico: Tip. José González Font, 1887; and Rigau-Pérez, J.G. "La salud ... siglo XX," op. cit.
67   Báguena Cervellera, María José. *La tuberculosis y su historia.* Barcelona: Fundación Uriach 1838, 1992; and Ott, Katherine. *Fevered Lives: Tuberculosis in American Culture since 1870.* Cambridge, Massachusetts: Harvard University Press, 1996.

combating the disease. The Townsend Report, as it came to be known, already mentioned above, concluded that there was great underreporting of disease; that the disease rate (the proportion of the population that developed tuberculosis) seemed to be similar in the United States and Puerto Rico (about 1.1%); but that the mortality rate (the proportion of the population that died of tuberculosis) was nearly twice that of the United States.[68] The numbers presented by Townsend for Puerto Rico are about 2,700 deaths in a population of 1,300,000, or 208 per hundred thousand whereas today a case incidence rate over 85 per hundred thousand is considered a serious tuberculosis problem.[69] Disease rates were higher in coastal regions and towns throughout the island where the tobacco industry was active. The principal predisposing conditions were family crowding in poor housing with little ventilation; malnutrition; work in the tobacco industry (where poor ventilation of work spaces was the rule, in contrast to the sugar or coffee workers, who worked mostly out of doors); and lack of treatment facilities, social workers, and infant welfare clinics. Transmission through milk was not considered a factor, because of safeguards in its production, but sadly also because there was so little consumption of

---

[68]　One of the Puerto Rican physicians O'Connor met, writing five years after Townsend, indicated that the mortality rate in urban areas of Puerto Rico was five times that of New York City, see Costa Mandry, Oscar. "Epidemiology of tuberculosis in Porto Rico. I. Mortality statistics." *PR Journal of Public Health and Tropical Medicine* 1928; 4: 3-13.

[69]　Pérez-Perdomo, Rosa and Pérez-Cardona, Cynthia M. "An epidemiological review of tuberculosis in the Puerto Rican population." *PR Health Sci J* 1999; 18: 117-122.

it.[70]

Even before the discovery by Robert Koch in 1882 of the bacterial cause of tuberculosis, the disease was considered to be associated with malnutrition and crowded housing, so treatment relied on rest, good diet, and exposure to sun and air. Mountain or beachside sanatoria were built for private and needy patients to provide the environment necessary for recovery.[71] The Puerto Rico Sanatorium was located on a low hill, separated from urban Río Piedras by sugarcane fields. This 103-acre farm was donated to the government in 1918 by Pedro Arzuaga Beraza (1863-1922) and the facility established was typical of the times in its emphasis on adequate diet, open landscape, and broad verandahs that allowed sleeping in the open air.[72]

In the five years between Townsend's and O'Connor's visits, the tuberculosis mortality rate in Puerto Rico increased by 50%. The Río Piedras Sanatorium (200 beds), the Ponce Sanatorium (30 beds), the five municipal and three private hospitals that admitted tuberculosis cases were inadequate for a problem that caused almost 4,000 deaths annually.[73]

---

70   The "safeguards" were related to general hygienic measures. Even by 1927, only two dairies (both in San Juan) distributed pasteurized milk. Molina Fernández, José F. *La industria lechera en Puerto Rico*. Miami, Nupress, 2001: 35.

71   The paradigmatic description of life in a tuberculosis sanatorium, Thomas Mann's novel, *The Magic Mountain*, was published in German in 1924 and in English in 1927.

72   Costa Mandry, O. *Apuntes*, op.cit.: 155; Comisionado de Sanidad. *Informe anual del Departamento de Sanidad de Puerto Rico*. Año fiscal 1917-1918. San Juan: Negociado de Materiales, Imprenta y Transporte, 1918: 56. The area is now occupied by the Puerto Rico Medical Center.

73   "El Sanatorio Insular está lleno y día tras día aumenta el número de solicitantes. El Comisionado de Sanidad ordena la salida de 105 pacientes que han estado allí más de un año." San Juan: *El Mundo*, 29 October 1927: 1, 11.

Townsend estimated that in 1922, only one case out of every 25 received treatment. In addition, by 1927, sanatoria were expected to provide more complex diagnostic and surgical services, but the lack of equipment and trained nurses resulted in poor quality of service for those lucky enough to be admitted.[74] Effective antimicrobial treatment for tuberculosis (streptomycin) became available in 1947, and quickly made sanatoria obsolete.[75] In recent years the incidence of tuberculosis in Puerto Rico has hovered around 7 cases per hundred thousand, with a mortality rate under 2 deaths per hundred thousand: still two to three times the average mortality rate for tuberculosis in the United States.[76]

Leprosy, also called Hansen disease in honor of the microbiologist who first isolated the causative organism, is a slow, chronic disease of the skin, peripheral nerves, and the upper airway. At the beginning of the twentieth century, leprosy patients in Puerto Rico were committed to Isla de Cabras, a rocky islet surrounded by heavy surf at the mouth of San Juan bay, to safeguard the healthy population from contagion and ostensibly to assist the sick. The ill-equipped,

---

74   Townsend, J.G. *Tuberculosis survey*, op.cit.: 57; Farley, J. *Rockefeller*, op.cit.: 185; and Lebrón-Rivera, Rafael. *¡Detengamos el jinete de la muerte! La lucha por controlar la tuberculosis en Puerto Rico, 1900-1940*. Thesis for the Master's Degree, Department of History, Humanities Faculty, University of Puerto Rico, Río Piedras Campus, 1990: 103.

75   Ryan, Frank. *The Forgotten Plague. How the Battle Against Tuberculosis was Won— and Lost*. Boston: Little, Brown, and Company, 1993: 282.

76   Pérez-Perdomo, R. and Pérez-Cardona, C.M. "An epidemiological review…," op. cit; and Pan American Health Organization, Area of Health Analysis and Information Systems (AIS). Regional Core Health Data Initiative; Technical Health Information System. Washington, DC; 2004: http://www.paho.org/English/SHA/coredata/tabulator/newTabulator.pdf (accessed 16 September 2005).

poorly maintained facility held 20 to 40 inmates.[77] No curative treatment existed, rehabilitation was not provided, and living conditions were unsanitary. This moved Manuel Quevedo Báez, the physician in charge in 1904, to call the leprosarium "a cemetery that buries men alive."[78] The Insular Legislature approved a process for the creation of a new facility only after a hurricane in 1916 caused great damage to the existing buildings. By this time, Congress had established a U.S. leprosarium (Carville, Louisiana, 1917), Evangelical Protestant churches had become advocates for the Isla de Cabras patients, and a promising treatment for leprosy offered the possibility of cure. It still took ten years to move patients from Isla de Cabras. A new leprosarium, located in a rural area of the municipality of Trujillo Alto (22 kilometers from San Juan), opened in June, 1926.[79] By 1928 it was full to capacity (60 patients) with a long waiting list for new admissions.

O'Connor describes an administration and laboratory building, the small houses for up to four patients each, and farm and garden plots.[80] The patients were treated with intramuscular injections of chaulmoogra oil, a product derived

---

77   Two recent articles summarize the recent history of leprosy in Puerto Rico: Vázquez, J., Lugo, A., Almodóvar, P.I. and Sánchez, J.L. "Leprosy in Puerto Rico (1901-2001)." *Bol Asoc Med P Rico* 2003; 95: 17-21; and Levison, Julie H. "Beyond quarantine: a history of leprosy in Puerto Rico, 1898-1930s." *História, Ciências, Saúde—Manguinhos* 2003; 10 (S. 1): 225-245.

78   Quevedo Báez, Manuel. "Juicios acerca del aislamiento y contagiosidad de la lepra." *Bol Asoc Med P Rico* 1904; 2 (17): 261-264. His opinion carried weight—he was president of the Puerto Rico Medical Association.

79   The institution occupied the southeast quadrant of the present intersection of Routes 199 and 845; some buildings still exist.

80   O'Connor. *Diary...* (November 12).

from the seeds of an Asian plant (*Hydnocarpus* species).[81] This traditional therapy was taken up by British physicians in India in the nineteenth century. By 1905 the Wellcome Chemical Research Laboratories in London had devised a pharmaceutical preparation. The oil gave encouraging (though never dramatically convincing) results in uncontrolled studies at Carville and later in Manila, while producing considerable discomfort to the patients, whether ingested or injected. At Carville, where chaulmoogra was used until 1947, patients could choose the route of administration.[82] When Ortiz told O'Connor that chaulmoogra's efficacy was overrated, he most likely referred to his own study, published four years before.[83] After a year and a half of treatment, young patients with a short history of illness saw notable improvement in the lesions, but all patients remained bacteriologically positive.

Unfortunately, the "admirable opportunity for research" and the "splendid laboratory facilities" mentioned by O'Connor[84] were not exploited. The institution only served to provide long-term care and confinement for patients. When Dr. Pedro Malaret became medical director in 1942, he found that the patient records, starting in 1926, were "rudimentary and unreliable, consisting of a few notes jotted down by one of the nurses." Chaulmoogra oil was still used, but "according to the whims of each particular

---

81   In 1917, patients at Isla de Cabras were already receiving weekly injections of chaulmoogra oil, according to Zamacois, E. *La alegría de andar*, op. cit.: 132.

82   Parascandola, John. "Chaulmoogra oil and the treatment of leprosy." *Pharm Hist* 2003; 45 (2): 47-57.

83   Ortiz, Pedro N. "La lepra y su nuevo tratamiento." *Bol Asoc Med P Rico* 1923; 17 (141): 27-39 (with 27 patient photos).

84   O'Connor. *Diary…* (November 12).

patient" (similar to the situation at Carville, it turns out).[85] Efficacious treatment became available in 1946 with the use of glucosulfone (Promin), and improved as new antibiotics were developed. Therapy with multiple antibiotics later allowed patient management in ambulatory settings, so the Insular Leprocomium closed in 1977.[86] Studies of the total case load of leprosy patients in Puerto Rico published from 1928 to 1981 consistently resulted in an estimated prevalence of approximately 10 living patients per 100,000 population.[87] New cases are still diagnosed in Puerto Rico, although fewer, and of more advanced age than in previous decades.[88]

Syphilis is an acute and chronic bacterial disease transmitted by direct contact with infectious lesions during sexual intercourse or through transplacental infection of the

---

85   Malaret, Pedro J. "Leprosy in Puerto Rico." *Bol Asoc Med P Rico* 1951; 43: 15-64; and Parascandola, J. "Chaulmoogra oil…," op. cit.

86   See Torres, Víctor. *No quiero decir adiós: memorias de un hablador*. San Juan: Editorial Universidad de Puerto Rico, 2000: 498-499, for a dermatologist's account of the change from Leprosarium to "Dermatologic Center" and the eventual closure of the institution. His book of short stories (*Los porfíricos, y otros cuentos hipocráticos*. San Juan: private edition, 2001) includes a "fictional" account of an inmate's experience during the Leprosarium's last years (pages 15-46, "La revancha").

87   See: Palacios de Borao, Gonzalo. "An epidemiological study of leprosy in Puerto Rico with special reference to topographic and climatic factors." *PR Journal of Public Health and Tropical Medicine* 1928; 4: 20-45 (pages 27-39 reproduce 27 patient photos). The study was reported in greater detail in, "La lepra, enfermedad familiar. Estudio epidemiológico del problema en Puerto Rico (I)." *Bol Asoc Med P Rico* 1927 (158): 1-45 (includes four patient photos); "La lepra y las condiciones climáticas [en Puerto Rico II]." *Bol Asoc Med P Rico* 1927 (159): 3-58; Nine Curt, J., Torres, V.N. and Leopold, N.F. "Leprosy in Puerto Rico: a new look at an old disease." *Bol Asoc Med P Rico* 1968; 60: 53-61; and Ramos Caro, F., Sánchez, J.L., and Vázquez-Botet, M. "Incidence of leprosy in Puerto Rico. Update 1980." *Bol Asoc Med P Rico* 1981; 73: 488-496.

88   Vázquez, J. et al. "Leprosy in Puerto Rico," op. cit.; and Editors. Making progress towards leprosy elimination. *The Lancet* 2006; 367: 276.

fetus. The blood test for laboratory diagnosis used in 1927 was known as the Wassermann test. Treatment to arrest disease in the 1920s consisted of 20-40 intramuscular injections of an arsenical compound, neoarsphenamine, also known as neosalvarsan. These injections, often very painful, had to be supplemented by the application of mercury and bismuth ointments.[89] Penicillin is now the cure, but will not reverse late lesions. Morbidity statistics for syphilis in Puerto Rico in the 1920s are very erratic. The reports for fiscal years ending 1923 and 1925 do not even include this disease. The other years up to 1927 note 185 to 420 cases, except for 17 cases in 1921 and 2,444 in 1924. That year, both the reported cases (164) and the positive blood tests in the Department of Health's Biologic Laboratory were included in the tally.[90] In contrast to the United States, where syphilis was unmentionable in public and in the press up to the late 1930s, the newspapers in Puerto Rico frequently published advertisements and informational articles on treatment for syphilis.[91] Publications by local clinician

89   Jones, James H. *Bad Blood: The Tuskegee Syphilis Experiment.* New York: The Free Press, 1981: 46.

90   Comisionado de Sanidad. *Informe anual del Comisionado de Sanidad al Gobernador de Puerto Rico.* Año fiscal 1923 a 1924. San Juan: Negociado de Materiales, Imprenta y Transporte, 1925: 17.

91   Lederer, Susan E. and Parascandola, John. "Screening syphilis: Dr. Ehrlich's magic bullet meets the Public Health Service." *Journal of the History of Medicine and Allied Sciences* 1998; 53: 345-370; Benedek, Thomas G. and Erlen, Jonathon. "The scientific environment of the Tuskegee study of syphilis, 1920-1960." *Perspectives in Biology and Medicine* 1999; 43: 1-30; Advertisement for "Sulfarsenol del laboratorio Pluchon de París ... para la curación de la sífilis". *El Mundo,* San Juan, 22 October 1924: 7; "La espantosa situación que atraviesa la salud pública". *El Mundo,* San Juan, 22 July 1925: 1,6; "La degeneración de un pueblo" [editorial]. *El Mundo,* San Juan, 23 July 1925: 2; Advertisement for Dr. M. Juliá: "Sífilis, especialmente del cerebro". *La Correspondencia de Puerto Rico,* San Juan, 6 October 1925: 4; and Carbonell, Diego, "Rector de la Universidad Central" [Caracas]. La medicina al día: Salvarsan o Novarsenobenzol. *La Democracia,* San Juan, 13 October 1925: 2.

researchers (for example, Dr. J.C. Ferrer, who claimed to have examined over 5,000 syphilitics in nine years of practice) suggest that the diagnosis was much more frequent than the morbidity statistics indicate (although the authors were at pains to indicate that the disease was less frequent than popularly stated).[92]

When yaws, a chronic relapsing infection, is mentioned in the diary, an unexpected statement makes the reader go back over the text to make sure there was no misunderstanding. On the trip along the northwest coast with Garry Burke, O'Connor notes: "Isabela [is] the only endemic area of yaws left on the island (this being allowed to continue under supervision for comparison and teaching purposes)."[93] To hold back preventive activities or treatment from a community so that cases of a disease may be available for study is unethical, even criminal, because the potential benefits of research cannot compensate the harm that comes to the members of the community. The infamous "Tuskegee study" of untreated syphilis in poor African American men in rural Alabama comes immediately to mind. This was a project established in 1932 when moderately efficacious treatments for syphilis were known but hardly available to farm laborers due to their cost and side effects. Not only were the patients in the Tuskegee study not treated with mercury, they were left untreated even after penicillin was easily available to cure syphilis.[94]

---

92   Ferrer, J. C. "Estudio de la sífilis en Puerto Rico." *Bol Asoc Med P Rico* 1926; 20 (152): 7-17; Serra, Américo. "La sífilis en Puerto Rico: su incidencia." *Bol Asoc Med P Rico* 1930; 22 (179): 151-155; and Costa, Mandry Oscar. "Syphilis in Porto Rico: I. Its prevalence as shown by the Wassermann reaction." *PR Journal of Public Health and Tropical Medicine* 1931; 7: 209-231.

93   O'Connor. *Diary...* (November 15).

94   Jones, J.H. *Bad Blood*, op. cit.; and Benedek, T.G. and Erlen, J. "The scientific environment...," op. cit.

Was there a yaws study in Isabela that would compare to the Tuskegee study? The government's disease incidence statistics for fiscal year 1919-20 to 1945 indicate no cases of yaws reported in that municipality. Only 1 or 2 cases were reported in Puerto Rico, until an outbreak in Utuado in 1931 produced 83 cases (of the 92 reported for the island). In the next three years, 57 cases were reported. From 0 to 3 cases were reported every year thereafter until 1945, following which no more cases were noted.[95] The explanation of O'Connor's statement is found in the report of the investigation of the Utuado outbreak. The authors refer to yaws in Puerto Rico as a medical curiosity.

> It was known in a coastal community in the north-
> western part of the Island [evidently, Isabela], and
> interested physicians sought patients there when
> they were required for study or demonstrations,
> but no effort was made to eradicate the infection
> or to locate other affected communities. It was
> recognized from general clinical observations
> that the disease was not a serious problem to the
> Island...Occasional cases of the disease were also
> now and then found in Coamo, Peñuelas, and
> Carolina...[96]

---

95   *Annual Reports of the Governor of Porto Rico*, Washington, D.C.: Government Printing Office, 1920-1923; *Annual Reports of the Commissioner of Health of Puerto Rico*, San Juan: Bureau of Printing, Supplies, and Transportation/ Department of Health, 1924-1945.

96   Gotay, J.B., Costa Mandry, O. and Payne, G.C. "The intensive method of control applied to yaws." *PR Journal of Public Health and Tropical Medicine* 1935; 11: 91-101. Articles were published in English and Spanish; the original Spanish version (pages 102-113) provides further nuances.

A leading public health textbook of the time indicated that traveling clinics for the administration of salvarsan could control yaws in endemic areas, as "has been demonstrated in Santo Domingo".[97] That study actually reported that most patients improved after one injection of neosalvarsan, but only 176 (31%) of 570 were cured or practically cured. The authors stated that the result of "treatment in our series is of little value owing to the limited time over which cases were observed and the fact that many patients received but a single treatment and were not seen again".[98] The Utuado outbreak control effort was carried out by the Department of Health with the assistance of the International Health Division of Rockefeller Foundation, which at that time was very interested in the disease in Jamaica.[99] It included the treatment of many cases with neoarsphenamine and three years of follow-up. The investigators were not satisfied with the results, and concluded that "more intensive treatment must be directed toward the known cases to rid the community of the infection."[100] O'Connor's statement on yaws is therefore inaccurate on several counts. Isabela was not the only, but the best known, endemic area of yaws on the island, because of prior outbreaks (1902, 1917).[101] There was no yaws elimination program in Puerto Rico, probably because the available treatment for yaws was not entirely efficacious, and

97   Rosenau, Milton J. *Preventive Medicine and Hygiene*, 5th ed. New York: D. Appleton and Co., 1928: 412.

98   Moss, W.L. and Bigelow, G.H. "Yaws: an analysis of 1046 cases in the Dominican Republic." *Johns Hopkins Hospital Bulletin* 1922; 33: 43-55.

99   Farley, J. *Rockefeller*, op.cit.: 190.

100   Gotay, J.B. et al., "The intensive method...," op. cit.

101   Comisionado de Sanidad. "*Informe anual...1917-1918*," op. cit.: [Framboesia] 77-83.

because acute diseases with higher lethality consumed all public health efforts.

The examination of the context of O'Connor's comment highlights two conditions of public health work in Puerto Rico in 1927. First, disease surveillance statistics (for example, reported cases of yaws in Isabela) were a poor reflection of reality or of the knowledge of physicians. Second, the work was carried out with a condescendence (that might be called indifference) towards the "revolting states of illness"[102] in which the poorest citizens lived and died. Even though yaws was not considered a serious problem to the island, the lesions were destructive and disfiguring, as the photos of patients in the 1917 and 1931 outbreaks show. The apparent indifference with which O'Connor recorded his comments could be an example of what historian Susan Lederer has called "the racialized dimensions of research and the social distance between investigators and their research subjects" in the interwar years.[103] Unfortunately, it is not difficult to find evidence of what researchers thought was only light-hearted or playful, and what she calls their "casual appropriation of the bodies of people of color" before that time and even in medical schools attended by Puerto Ricans.[104] Historians Marcos Cueto and John Farley, too,

---

102   Citing O'Connor's words about La Perla. O'Connor. *Diary...* (November 11).

103   Lederer, Susan E. "'Porto Ricochet': Joking about germs, cancer, and race extermination in the 1930s." *American Literary History* 2002; 14: 720-746.

104   Fay, D. Edgar. "Senior medical class prophecy." In: Audet, Charles H. and Makover, A.B. eds. *Terra Mariae 1917* [Yearbook of the graduating classes of the Medical, Dental, Pharmacy, and Law Schools of the University of Maryland]. Baltimore, MD; American Printing Co., 1917: 84-94, esp. 89: "One of Surgeon Shinn's most notable feats, in the way of public health and sanitation, was the extermination of the "Populus Nigri" from the City of Washington."

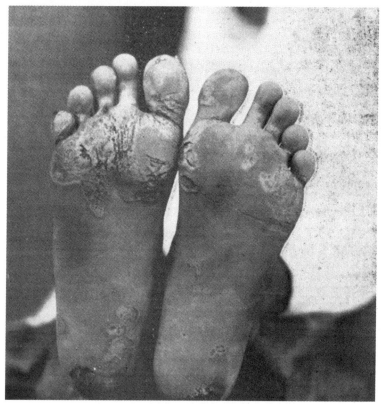

Grandomas infiltrados llamados "clavos"
(Informe Anual Comisionado de Sanidad 1917-18.)

in their accounts of Rockefeller Foundation projects have
found examples of the effect of racist bias on reports and
administrative decisions.[105]

Parasitic diseases transmitted by mosquitoes

In almost all of these diseases, the initial infection
usually produces a short, undifferentiated febrile illness, or
may be asymptomatic. Malaria may produce life-threatening

---

105   Cueto, Marcos. "Visions of science and development: the Rockefeller Foundation's Latin American surveys of the 1920s." In: Cueto, M. *Missionaries of science*,
op.cit.: 1-22; and Farley, J. *Rockefeller*, op.cit.: 191-192.

syndromes on first infection. Prevention and control efforts for these conditions have two equally important priorities: accurate diagnosis and treatment, and identification and elimination of the mosquitoes. O'Connor's reports of activities related to filariasis and malaria therefore include a discussion of clinical, laboratory, and entomological issues.

Malaria, with case-fatality ratios of 10-40% if untreated,[106] was an important health problem in Puerto Rico as well as in the southern United States.[107] The diagnosis of malaria requires an examination of the patient's blood to detect the parasite. When O'Connor wrote about thick and thin films during his visit to Fajardo,[108] he was referring to special preparations required to be able to effect a microscopic diagnosis.[109] To define the frequency and distribution of the malaria problem, public health researchers need to determine the proportion infected among the general population (or among special groups such as small children). This requires obtaining information from apparently healthy individuals, who usually object to giving blood, even by fingerstick. The "splenic index," criticized by Earle and O'Connor,[110] was an alternative painless indicator of malaria prevalence,

106   Guerin, P.J., Olliaro, P., Nosten, F., Druilhe, P., Laxminarajan, R., Binka, F., Kila-ma, W.L., Ford N., White, N.J. "Malaria: current status of control, diagnosis, treatment, and a proposed agenda for research and development." *Lancet Infect Dis* 2002 Sep; 2 (9): 564-573; and Murphy, S.C. and Breman, J.G. "Gaps in the childhood malaria burden in Africa: cerebral malaria, neurological sequelae, anemia, respiratory distress, hypoglyce-mia, and complications of pregnancy." *Am J Trop Med Hyg* 2001; 64 (1, 2) S: 57-67.

107   Humphreys, Margaret. *Malaria: Poverty, race, and public health in the United States*. Baltimore: Johns Hopkins University Press, 2001.

108   O'Connor. *Diary...* (November 7).

109   Boyd, Mark ed. *Malariology*. Philadelphia: WB Saunders, 1949: 158-159.

110   O'Connor. *Diary...* (November 3).

which could be obtained by palpating a child's abdomen to detect an enlarged spleen.[111] The method had recently been proposed by a Rockefeller Foundation colleague, Dr. Samuel Darling,[112] an acquaintance of both O'Connor and one of his dinner hosts (Dr. Walter Glines).[113]

Walter C. Earle conducted studies on malaria in Puerto Rico from 1924 to 1935, and headed the Department of Health's Bureau of Malaria Control from 1929 to 1932.[114] In Fajardo he quickly shared with O'Connor the essential facts of the local malaria problem, but O'Connor took down the wrong information when he noted the parasite ratio. Earle recognized that *Plasmodium falciparum* was more frequent than *P. vivax*. Its cases peaked in December, while *P. vivax* peaked in October or November (the time of O'Connor's visit) and was relatively more frequent than *P. falciparum* only from May to August.[115] Earle used, among other data, results from the "precipitin method" described so minutely by O'Connor to show that the only significant anopheline vector was *Anopheles albimanus. A. grabhami* and *A. vestitipennis*, although potential carriers, were actually not involved in human

111   Ibid.: 849.
112   Farley, J. *Rockefeller*, op.cit.: 66, 118, 205.
113   O'Connor. *Diary...* (November 1).
114   Commissioner of Health of Porto Rico. *Report of the Commissioner of Health of Porto Rico for the Fiscal Year ending 1930*. San Juan: Bureau of Supplies, Printing, and Transportation, 1931: 3; Commissioner of Health of Porto Rico. *Report of the Commissioner of Health to the Governor of Porto Rico for the Fiscal Year ending June 30, 1932*. San Juan: Bureau of Supplies, Printing, and Transportation, 1933: 5; and Palacios, Luis D. *Informe sobre la lucha antimalárica en Puerto Rico* [1925-1955]. San Juan: Departamento de Salud [mimeographed], 1961: 95, 146.
115   Earle, Walter C. "The epidemiology of malaria with special reference to Puerto Rico." *PR Journal of Public Health and Tropical Medicine* 1939; 15: 3-27.

malaria.[116] The precipitin method used a chemical reaction to identify the source of blood meal for mosquitoes (that's why the ingredients included human, horse, and ox serum). If the gut content of mosquitoes was animal blood, they were not biting humans, and therefore not involved in the transmission of the disease.[117]

A. albimanus, as O'Connor noted, breeds in most kinds of water, even water with relatively high salinity. Its larvae grow in marshes, ponds, creeks, pools and ditches, such as used in sugar cane cultivation, and they have a marked preference for sunlit, stagnant or very slowly moving water.[118] Earle's studies were conducted on the plantations of two of the four largest sugar corporations, Fajardo Sugar in the northeast, and Central Aguirre Sugar in the southeast, which provided some logistical support.[119] All sugar cultivation areas, not just Fajardo, had, as O'Connor puts it, "a big malaria problem."[120] In fact, these areas were an important cause of the increase in malaria incidence in Puerto Rico. Sugarcane cultivation was made possible in the southern coastal valleys by the construction of a large network of irrigation ditches. The effect of irrigation was particularly studied during the decade following O'Connor's 1927 visit. It could be shown that urban areas near irrigated

---

116   Earle, Walter C. "Malaria in Porto Rico." *Am J Trop Med* 1930; 10: 207-230; and Earle, Walter C. *Anopheles grabhami* (Theobald), a possible vector of malaria. *Bol Asoc Med P Rico* 1936; 28: 228-232.

117   Boyd, M. *Malariology*, op.cit.: 357-361.

118   Ibid.: 766.

119   Ayala, C. *American Sugar*, op.cit.: 108.

120   O'Connor. *Diary…* (November 7).

sugarcane lands (i.e., Guayama and Ponce) had an average malaria mortality rate (387 per 100,000) almost three times the malaria mortality rate for urban areas near non-irrigated sugarcane lowlands (Aguadilla, Arecibo, and Mayagüez, 136 per 100,000) and almost eight times the rate in urban areas with little or no low-lying sugar cane land nearby (Bayamón, Caguas, Río Piedras, San Juan, 51 per 100,000).[121] Irrigation not only brought water to previously dry lands, but also created irrigated valleys near extensive mangroves which extended the mosquitoes' breeding grounds. The precarious living conditions of workers offered no protection against mosquito bites. As O'Connor concisely noted: "We visited many breeding places and areas where humans herd and everywhere the conditions were the same—bad."[122]

The history of the emergence and elimination of malaria in Puerto Rico has not been written.[123] A Division for the Extermination of Mosquitoes was established in the

---

121   *Report of the Commissioner of Health of Porto Rico for the fiscal year ending 1925 to the Governor of Porto Rico.* San Juan: Bureau of Supplies, Printing, and Transportation, 1926: 84—[In Fajardo,] "the problem is one of control of mosquitoes in water which is the result of irrigation and heavy rains."; Earle, Walter C. "Malaria in Porto Rico in its relation to the cultivation of sugar cane." *Southern Medical Journal* 1930; 23: 449-452; and Henderson, John M. "Urban malaria in Puerto Rico." *PR Journal of Public Health and Tropical Medicine* 1942; 17: 278-288.

122   O'Connor. *Diary...* (November 7).

123   An extensive report by Luis Palacios (*Informe,* op. cit.) provides a summary of Department of Health activities from 1925 to 1955. It doesn't cover activities before the establishment of a Bureau of Malaria Control, nor activities by the Rockefeller Foundation and School of Tropical Medicine staff, the armed forces, and the World War II era agency known as "Malaria Control in War Areas."

Department of Health in 1911.[124] Considerable attention was given to sanitary precautions in the design of houses and the elimination of mosquito production sites.[125] In the city of Ponce, and presumably in other municipalities as well, architectural plans had to be approved by the municipal hygiene officer. In the 1921 design for a Ponce house with an indoor fountain, the architect wrote "with tropical fish to destroy mosquito larvae."[126] The first assessment of malaria endemicity was apparently carried out in 1919-1920. The Department of Health asked for the Rockefeller Foundation's collaboration in evaluating the public health impact of malaria and also hookworm (discussed below).[127] The survey, conducted also with the support of some sugar corporations, found that in the coastal areas at least 25% of the population was infected, and in some workers' colonies near or on sugar

---

124   Dirección de Sanidad. *Informe anual* [1911-1912, Servicio Sanitario de la Isla de Puerto Rico]. San Juan: Negociado de Materiales, Imprenta y Transporte, 1912: 5-8.

125   In 1916, Dr. William F. Lippitt threatened the Catholic bishop of Puerto Rico with a fine, because holy water founts were harboring mosquito larvae. Luis P. Sánchez-Longo, "Monseñor William Jones: ¿Hombre al servicio de Dios o del César?", In: García-Colón, P. et al., *Tras las huellas del pasado*. San Juan: Isla Negra, 2000: 39-64.

126   Archivo Histórico de Ponce. Plans for the Juan Bigas residence, by Architect Blas Silva, 1921.

127   Comisionado de Sanidad. *Informe del Comisionado de Sanidad de Puerto Rico*. Año fiscal de 1919-1920. San Juan: Negociado de Materiales, Imprenta y Transporte, 1920: 6-7; and *Report of the Commissioner of Health of Porto Rico* [1920] 1921. Bureau of Insular Affairs, War Department, Washington, DC: Government Printing Office, 1923: 81. It was the Foundation's first field assignment for Dr. John B. Grant, whose 40-year career influenced public health systems from China to Czechoslovakia (and in mid-century, again Puerto Rico). See Farley, J. *Rockefeller*, op.cit.: 14-16, 299.

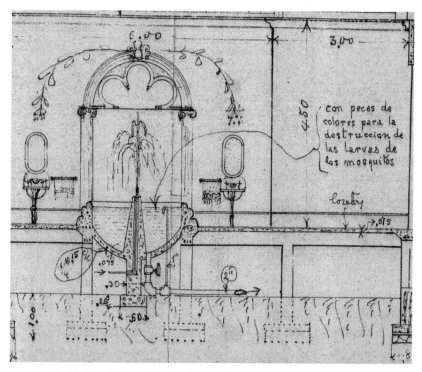

(Archivo hitsórico de Ponce. Plans for the Juan Bigas residence, by Architect Blas Silva.)

plantations, the parasite rate reached 70%.[128] The studies of malaria in high incidence areas in Puerto Rico that the Rockefeller Foundation had sponsored in the early 1920s were followed by the creation of a Bureau of Malaria Control in the Department of Health. Beginning with a demonstration unit in Fajardo in 1925, the Bureau quickly expanded its activities

128   Clark, V.S. *Porto Rico and its Problems*, op. cit.: 64. The original report is by John B. Grant (1920). International Health Board Report number 7525: Report of hookworm infection survey and malaria survey of Puerto Rico, December 26, 1919-January 28, 1920. New York (mimeographed). Rockefeller Foundation Archives, Tarrytown, New York.

to the south coast.[129] Specific actions to suppress mosquitoes in the early twentieth century included the elimination of household breeding (water collecting) sites through sealing, draining, elimination, or oiling of the contents causing larval death by asphyxiation. Later anti-malaria activity included the application of an arsenic-based compound (Paris green, copper acetoarsenite) to kill *Anopheles* larvae in the water, drainage of swampy areas, and treatment of cases. In 1927, patients were treated with quinine capsules for at least two months.[130]

With the onset of World War II, the federal government undertook major drainage projects for the establishment of military installations and in areas near existing military bases to protect enlisted personnel, while the Department of Health extended its malaria case treatment efforts.[131] Dichlorodiphenyltrichloroethane (DDT), a new long-lasting insecticide developed during the war years,

---

129   Franco Agudelo, S. *El paludismo en América Latina.* Guadalajara: Ed. Universidad de Guadalajara, 1990: 95, 221, 223; Commissioner of Health of Porto Rico. *Report of the Commissioner of Health of Porto Rico to the Governor of Porto Rico for the Fiscal Year ending June 30, 1926.* San Juan: Bureau of Supplies, Printing, and Transportation, 1927: 48; and Commissioner of Health of Porto Rico. *Report of the Commissioner of Health of Porto Rico for the Fiscal Year ending 1927.* San Juan: Bureau of Supplies, Printing, and Transportation, 1929:62-95.

130   Farley, J. *Rockefeller,* op.cit.: 112-113; Earle, W.C. "Malaria in Porto Rico...," op.cit.; and Commissioner of Health of Porto Rico. *Report for Fiscal Year ending June 30, 1926;* 51.

131   Henderson, John M. "Antimalaria measures for the protection of military personnel in Puerto Rico and their applicability to civilian malaria control." *PR Journal of Public Health and Tropical Medicine* 1945; 20: 419-445; Bureau of Malaria and Insect Control, Puerto Rico Department of Health. "Malaria control in Puerto Rico (a summary of accomplishments) 1924-1954." *Bol Of Sanit Panam* 1955; 39: 489-493; and Palacios, L. *Informe,* op.cit.: 304-305.

proved so effective that it was called the "master key to all the different problems" [in malaria control]; "the answer to the health workers' prayer;" and even "the atomic bomb of the insect world."[132] Unfortunately, DDT is also extraordinarily long-lasting, accumulates in the fatty tissue of animals and humans, and may disrupt hormonal balance.[133] It was first used in Puerto Rico in 1944, and quickly adopted by the Bureau of Malaria Control for what it called "dedetización"— DDTzation. The last autochthonous case of malaria in Puerto Rico was reported in 1953.[134]

Filariasis holds a key position in the history of infectious disease and in O'Connor's diary. It was in filariasis that mosquitoes were first shown to transmit disease (Patrick Manson in China, 1877). It was also in filariasis that O'Connor (Manson's pupil) developed his principal expertise in parasitic diseases, and that he conducted studies during his four visits to Puerto Rico. *Wuchereria bancrofti* (the parasite present in Puerto Rico in O'Connor's day), *Brugia malayi*, or *B. timori* larvae, transmitted by mosquitoes, lodge

---

132   The first two statements, by Lewis Hackett and Frederick L. Soper, respectively, are quoted by Farley, J. *Rockefeller*, op.cit.: 144. The third, quoted by Humphreys, M. *Malaria*, op.cit.: 147, comes from an anonymous editorial, "Taking stock of DDT." *Am J Public Health* 1946; 36: 657-658.

133   Turusov, V., Rakitsky, V. and Tomatis, L. "Dichlorodiphenyltrichloroethane (DDT): ubiquity, persistence, and risks." *Environmental Health Perspectives* 2002; 110: 125-128.

134   Palacios, L. *Informe*, op.cit.: 4, 296, 311. The 1955 report by the Bureau of Malaria and Insect Control, op. cit., indicates DDT was first used by the Department in 1954 but this is evidently a typographical error for 1945.

in the lymph tissue and the lungs and produce significant symptoms and incapacitation.[135] The dead *W. bancrofti* elicit an inflammatory reaction that obstructs the flow of lymph. This accumulates in the abdomen, groin or scrotum. Burke in Aguadilla "tapped," presumably with a needle and syringe, the hydroceles (collections of fluid inside the scrotal sac) of four male patients, but O'Connor failed to find microfilariae in any of them. With prolonged pressure from accumulated lymph fluid, the skin easily becomes infected and ulcerated. Tissue scarring results in elephantiasis, a dramatic enlargement of a leg, the scrotum, or vulva. The severe manifestations of lymphatic filariasis are usually the result of repeated infections that are active for years. There was no medication to treat filariasis in 1927. At present, drug treatment will clear most microfilariae from the blood, but may not destroy all adult worms, so it must be repeated at yearly intervals.[136]

According to Commissioner Ortiz in 1927, "filariasis and its sequelae, so common, remain unconquered as the disease does not cause so much physical disability and the mortality from direct causes is low. The people and the sanitary authorities do not seem to give much consideration to this disease as there is no specific treatment…"[137] This is

---

135 Melrose, W.D. "Lymphatic filariasis: new insights into an old disease." *Int J Parasitol* 2002; 32: 947-960.

136 Dreyer, G., Addiss, D., Dreyer, P. and Norões J. *Basic lymphoedema management: Treatment and prevention of problems associated with lymphatic filariasis.* Hollis, NH: Hollis Publishing Co., 2002.

137 Ortiz, P.N. "The tropics…," op. cit.: 6.

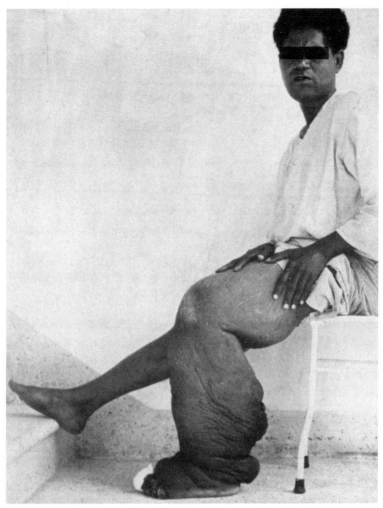

Filariasis
(O'Connor, F.W. and Hulse, C.R. "Studies in Filariasis I. In Puerto Rico."
Puerto Rico Journal of Public Health and Tropical Medicine 1935; 11: 167-272.)

a surprising statement, considering the many publications
by local investigators, and the appearance of the patients
O'Connor saw.[138] Filariasis was present throughout Puerto

138   See bibliography in Hoffman, W.A., Marín, R.A. and Burke, A.M.B. "Filariasis
in Porto Rico." *PR Journal of Public Health and Tropical Medicine* 1932; 7: 321-358.

Rico, with a few high intensity foci such as Puerta de Tierra (a very densely populated working-class suburb of San Juan bordering the bay) and Aguadilla (in the northwestern corner of the island).[139] As O'Connor stated in his November 7 lecture,[140] the mosquito responsible for transmission in Puerto Rico was unproven until he found filarial larvae in *Culex fatigans*, now called *C. quinquefasciatus*, collected at the Asilo de Niños.[141] This mosquito is common throughout the tropics and throughout Puerto Rico. The Asilo, or "Boys Charity School," where O'Connor collected human blood samples and mosquitoes infected with microfilariae, housed about 400 orphans and was located in Santurce, a populous area of San Juan (specifically, trolley stop 19 on Ponce de León Avenue). The risk of filaria transmission was therefore not limited to rural, poor, or markedly unsanitary areas. Cases were occasionally also diagnosed in members of the higher socioeconomic levels of society.[142] The development of specific antifilarial medications, aggressive antimosquito campaigns, and the general improvement in living conditions in Puerto Rico in the 1940s resulted in reduced infectivity in patients, smaller mosquito populations, and less exposure

---

139   Suárez, Jenaro. "A preliminary report on the clinical and bacteriological findings in 60 cases of lymphangitis associated with elephantoid fever in Porto Rico." *Am J Trop Med* 1930; 10: 183-198.

140   O'Connor. *Diary*…

141   O'Connor, Francis W. "Filariasis in association with infection of Filaria bancrofti." *PR Journal of Public Health and Tropical Medicine* 1927; 3 (6): 211-222.

142   Baralt, Guillermo A. *La vida de Luis A. Ferré*. 2 vols. San Juan: El Nuevo Día, 1996-1998; Vol. 1: 75.

to mosquito bites. The last case of filariasis diagnosed in Puerto Rico was reported in 1955.[143]

O'Connor's lectures were featured in newspapers twice—first announced, then chronicled.[144] It is not surprising, then, that an opinionated physician would call him to propose an original theory. I have found no information on "Dr. Birdwell," so it is not possible to tell why O'Connor found him "strange" or what exactly was his "opinion on filariasis."[145] The mention of inguinal (groin) glands and their inflammation (adenitis) suggests Birdwell may have attributed elephantiasis to the obstruction of lymph flow at the groin. The relative contribution of lymph obstruction, repeated bacterial infections, and formation of scar tissue to the development of elephantiasis was at the time being

---

143   Unpublished data, Communicable Disease Control Program, Puerto Rico Department of Health, 1979. I disregard the last case reported in a Secretary's Annual Report (Guillermo Arbona. *Informe Anual del Secretario de Salud*. Año fiscal 1957-1958. San Juan: Departamento de Salud, 1958:18), for 1956, because the Communicable Diseases Program had no evidence of its occurrence, suggesting a typographical error at press time. Palacios, L. *Informe*, op. cit., p. 287, reports a similar error in the Secretary's report for 1954-55, in which data for the previous year were repeated as current.

144   Anon. "El Dr. O'Connor de la 'Fundación Rockefeller', llegó ayer a San Juan." *El Mundo*, San Juan, 1 November 1927: 6; "La conferencia del Dr. O'Connor en la 'Escuela de Medicina Tropical', Ecos de Sociedad—Dr. F. W. O'Connor." *El Mundo*, San Juan, 3 November 1927: 5, 9; "La conferencia de esta noche en la 'Escuela de Medicina Tropical' [Disentería amébica]." *El Mundo*, San Juan, 14 November 1927: 5; "El Dr. O'Connor dictará esta noche su última conferencia." *El Mundo*, San Juan, 16 November 1927: 6; "Fue muy interesante la última conferencia del Dr. O'Connor en la 'Escuela de Medicina Tropical'." "Detalles de la vida en Samoa. Allí la mujer enamora al hombre." *El Mundo*, San Juan, 19 November 1927: 3.

145   O'Connor. *Diary...* (November 12).

elucidated.[146] Another example of the fluid state of knowledge for the diseases O'Connor mentions in his diary—even for conditions he knew well—is his statement in Aguadilla that "men are more frequently infected with filariasis than women."[147] In his extensive article summarizing several years' work in Puerto Rico published in 1935, O'Connor notes that filariasis was most prevalent among professional laundresses and their families.[148] Gender preference was not an intrinsic characteristic of the biological determinants of disease, but rather an accident of social conditions. It may be that in the countries O'Connor had visited before 1927, men were more exposed to infected mosquito bites than were women, but that was not the case in Puerto Rico.

Intestinal nematode infections transmitted through skin contact or ingestion

Hookworm disease (uncinariasis, by *Ancylostoma duodenale* and *Necator americanus*) affects the patient by producing significant anemia and low blood albumin. Prevention of hookworm disease rests on the sanitary disposal of feces (latrines, pit privies, or sanitary sewer systems) and the use of shoes. Specific diagnosis of the infecting parasite can be made by the identification of the distinctive eggs by microscopic examination of human

---

146   O'Connor, Francis W. and Hulse, Constance R. "Studies in filariasis. I. In Puerto Rico." *PR Journal of Public Health and Tropical Medicine* 1935; 11: 167-272, esp. 269. See also Hoffman, W.A., Marín, R.A. and Burke, A.M.B. "Filariasis in Porto Rico," op. cit.; and Martínez-Álvarez, A. "Observaciones clínico-microscópicas sobre la filariasis." *Bol Asoc Med PR* 1916; 13; 17-21.

147   O'Connor. *Diary...* (November 15).

148   O'Connor, F.W. and Hulse, C.R. Ibid.: 269.

fecal specimens. Treatment consists of oral vermifuges to eliminate the worms, and iron supplementation of the diet to relieve the anemia.

The first tropical parasite that O'Connor examined in Puerto Rico was an intestinal worm,[149] and the first public health program he describes was the hookworm elimination campaign.[150] The hookworm control efforts in Puerto Rico prompted the first contact of Rockefeller Foundation officials with the island's public health programs in 1908. Ironically, the next contact, in 1919, came when the Commissioner of Health asked the Foundation's International Health Board to study hookworm infection on the island because, despite all previous activities, the rate of infection remained over 80%.[151]

Dr. Bailey K. Ashford's hookworm work was directed at the reduction of mortality, which was caused, as he saw it, by hookworm infestation. His initial experiences in Ponce (1899, 1902-1903) and later in Bayamón, Utuado and Aibonito (1904-1906) provided evidence of the almost miraculous recovery of anemic patients, adequately diagnosed, and given the simple and inexpensive treatment of an oral dose of thymol to pass the worms in the stool.[152] Massive epidemics with high mortality are usually the result of a combination of

---

149 In an autopsy conducted by Lambert. O'Connor. *Diary...* (October 31).

150 Directed by Dr. Manuel Román Benítez. O'Connor. *Diary...* (November 1).

151 Arbona, Guillermo and Ramírez de Arellano, Annette B. *Regionalization of health services: The Puerto Rican experience*. New York: Oxford University Press, 1972: 10-11.

152 Simple but unpleasant; see Farley, J. *Rockefeller*, op. cit.: 32, for a description of the purge with Epsom salts.

microbiologic and social forces.[153] The lethal quality of the hookworm epidemic in those years (not seen in other populations with similar worm burdens) may have been due to two additional factors—acute famine and a coexistent epidemic of tropical sprue, an intestinal condition characterized by diarrhea, weight loss, and anemia.[154] The anemia of the field hands had been remarked upon, and even explained as uncinariasis, many years before Ashford's discovery.[155] Eight decades later it was postulated that the simultaneous presence of another intestinal ailment, sprue, could have accounted for some of the characteristics of the problem that Ashford and his colleagues tackled. The Anemia Clinics treated tens of thousands of patients and saved thousands of lives. Annual deaths attributed to hookworm fell from 7,369 in 1899 to 483 in 1928.[156] Nevertheless, hookworm infestation remained an intractable problem because patients

---

153   Bernabeu Mestre, Josep. *Enfermedad y población: Introducción a los problemas y métodos de la epidemiología histórica*. Valencia: Seminari d'Estudis sobre la Ciència, 1995: 77. Farley, J. *Rockefeller*, op.cit.: 288-299, summarizes recent historical research on the many forces shaping some twentieth century epidemics addressed by the Rockefeller Foundation.

154   Rigau-Pérez, José G. "Bailey K. Ashford, más allá de sus memorias." *P Rico Health Sci J* 2000; 19: 51-55; and Crosby, W.H. "The deadly hookworm: Why did the Puerto Ricans die?" *Arch Intern Med* 1987; 147: 577-578.

155   Leonard Reyes, Harold E. *El impacto de la campaña contra la uncinariasis y la política de salud pública norteamericana en Puerto Rico, 1898-1918*. Master's Thesis, History Department, Humanities Faculty, University of Puerto Rico, 1991: 71-73; Trigo, Benigno. "Anemia and vampires: figures to govern the colony, Puerto Rico, 1880 to 1904." *Comparative Studies in Society and History* 1999; 41: 104-123; and Agustín Stahl. "1890—Primer caso registrado en Puerto Rico de leucemia y hepar adiposum por uncinariasis." In Manuel Quevedo Báez. *Historia de la medicina y cirugía de Puerto Rico*, 2 vols. Santurce, P. R.: Asociación Médica de Puerto Rico, 1946-49; 1: 411-417. The title is misleading; the text makes clear that a fecal examination, because of the patient's anemia, revealed abundant "uncinaria" and *Ascaris*. Treatment with thymol resulted in the purge of the worms, but the patient died of leukemia.

156   Clark, V.S. *Porto Rico and its Problems*, op.cit.: 65.

were quickly reinfested upon entering their contaminated home environments. The social burden of hookworm changed from high mortality to high morbidity—many people infected, with adverse effects on physical and intellectual development. As a result, Victor Heiser, one of the highly influential Rockefeller Foundation staff officers, who participated with John B. Grant in the 1919 malaria and hookworm survey in Puerto Rico, judged that because of reinfestation, the hookworm treatment campaigns on the island had been a failure.[157] Even two decades later, the Puerto Rican rural laborer was still described as "a being with a blood that barely colors red the laboratory glass slide, who tastes no meat but the emergency ration distributed by the Red Cross the week after a hurricane."[158] The provision of treatment, specific education, shoes, and latrines, interventions targeted at interrupting the transmission of disease, were the methods recommended by Rockefeller Foundation-sponsored programs not only in Puerto Rico (as seen by O'Connor)[159] but also throughout the world.[160] By the 1960s, when shoes and adequate sanitary disposal of human feces became widely available on the island, intestinal parasites disappeared as an important source of illness.

Schistosomiasis (bilharziasis) is a blood flatworm infection in which parasites live for years within veins in the abdominal circulation (in the case of *Schistosoma mansoni* and *S. japonicum*)

---

157   Farley, J. *Rockefeller*, op.cit.: 71.

158   Belaval, Emilio S. *Cuentos para fomentar el turismo*. Barcelona: Rumbos, 1967 [originally published 1946]: 73.

159   O'Connor. *Diary...* (November 1).

160   Birn, Anne-Emanuelle and Solórzano, Armando. "Public health policy paradoxes: Science and politics in the Rockefeller Foundation's hookworm campaign in Mexico in the 1920s." *Social Science and Medicine* 1999; 49: 1197-1213; and Farley, J. *Rockefeller*, op.cit.: 61-87.

or urinary bladder veins (*S. haematobium*).[161] The occurrence of schistosomiasis in the Americas was discovered in 1904 by Dr. Isaac González Martínez, following his examinations of patients in Mayagüez, Puerto Rico.[162] At the beginning of the twentieth century, bilharzia was limited to three low-incidence mountainous locations in Puerto Rico (Mayagüez, Utuado, and Aibonito), and an area of high incidence, the island of Vieques. The change from coffee to sugarcane cultivation produced migrations of workers from the mountains to the coast, and the construction of large irrigation systems in the dry, southern plains. As a result, bilharzia spread throughout the island, with the highest incidence in the eastern regions (the Guayama area was considered the most important focus of transmission in the 1930s). The malaria eradication program of the federal government undertaken during World War II drained large areas of wetlands, contributing to the elimination of not only *Anopheles* but also *Schistosoma* habitats. In 1945 the Puerto Rico Aqueduct and Sewer Authority began a large-scale effort to provide potable water and proper disposal of human sewage to the entire population, probably the most effective way to decrease the contact of persons with the pathogen.[163] The next two decades also saw the disappearance

---

161   For a general history, see Farley, J. *Bilharzia*, op. cit.

162   González Martínez, Isaac. *La bilharziosis en Puerto Rico*. San Juan: Tipografía del Boletín Mercantil, 1904; and Faust, Ernest Carroll. "Studies on schistosomiasis mansoni in Puerto Rico. I.The history of schistosomiasis in Puerto Rico." *PR Journal of Public Health and Tropical Medicine* 1934: 154-162.

163   Bhajan, M.M., Martínez, V., Ruíz-Tibén, E. and Jobin W.R. "Socioeconomic changes and reduction in prevalence of schistosomiasis in Puerto Rico." *Bol Asoc Med P Rico* 1978; 70: 106-112; Jobin, William R. "Sugar and snails: The ecology of bilharziasis related to agriculture in Puerto Rico." *Am J Trop Med Hyg* 1980; 29: 86-94; and Haddock, Kenneth C. "Control of schistosomiasis: The Puerto Rican experience." *Social Science and Medicine* 1981; 15D: 501-514.

of the sugarcane industry in Puerto Rico. The incidence of reported disease peaked in the late 1950s, perhaps because years must elapse before the infection results in severe symptoms, or possibly because it was in 1953 that the Department of Health's Bilharzia Control Program was established. Its activities combined community education, provision of potable water, use of sanitary latrines, snail elimination, and treatment of infected persons.[164] In spite of the persistence of *Biomphalaria* in some locations, acute cases of schistosomiasis have become extremely rare, and the infection perhaps does not occur in Puerto Rico any more.[165]

Other important diseases briefly mentioned in the diary

O'Connor gives scant attention to diarrheal and nutritional diseases even though he notes on the first day of his visit that "the commonest causes of death in children are marasmus and the infantile diarrheas."[166] Marasmus, amebiasis,[167] and typhoid fever are briefly noted.

Three other diseases (pellagra, rickets, and sprue) are barely mentioned, not only because of their low incidence, but because O'Connor (and medical science) were just beginning to understand the role of vitamins in the maintenance of health.[168]

---

164   Rigau-Pérez, J.G. and Pereira Díaz, L.A. "¡HAY BILHARZIA!, by Klock, Ildefonso, and Mateo-Serrano: Medical images of poverty and development in Puerto Rico in the 1950s." *PR Health Sci J* 1996; 15: 33-44.

165   Hillyer, G.V. "The rise and fall of bilharzia in Puerto Rico: Its centennial 1904-2004." *PR Health Sci J* 2005; 24: 225-235.

166   O'Connor. *Diary...* (October 31).

167   The subject of O'Connor's lecture on November 14. O'Connor. *Diary*.

168   Cook, Donald H. and Rivera, Trinita. "A brief discussion of vitamins A, B, C, and D." *PR Journal of Public Health and Tropical Medicine* 1928; 3: 267-278.

Pellagra is a condition that produces diarrhea, psychic changes, and skin peeling (*pell'agra* in Italian means rough skin).[169] In O'Connor's time it was the subject of complex epidemiologic studies to elucidate its cause.[170] It is now known to be due to the lack of niacin, an amino acid of the vitamin B group of organic substances that must be present in the diet for normal metabolic functioning. Rickets, which results in weak and deformed bones, is usually due to lack of exposure to sunlight or lack of Vitamin D in the diet, but rare cases are due to congenital metabolic disturbances. O'Connor's note about "no true rickets,"[171] which may seem ridiculous in a Caribbean island, alludes to a recent investigation not mentioned in the diary. Vital statistics reports giving rickets as a cause of death were found to be mistranslated from the Spanish term "raquítico" (weak, stunted), and the examination of patients found no evidence of rickets.[172]

Sprue, as already indicated, is an intestinal disease characterized by chronic diarrhea, marked weight loss, and anemia. As O'Connor noted, two key symptoms were not seen in Puerto Rican sprue: tetany (muscle spasms in thorax and abdomen; not to be confused with the disease

169   Gutiérrez Igaravídez, P. "Un caso de pellagra." *Anales Médicos de Puerto Rico* 1912; 1: 35-42.
170   Kraut, Alan M. *Goldberger's war. The life and work of a public health crusader.* New York: Hill and Wang, 2003.
171   O'Connor. *Diary...* (November 2).
172   Fernós Isern, Antonio. "Infant mortality in Porto Rico." *PR Health Review* 1925; 1 (1): 3-10; and Eliot, Martha. "Observations on rickets." *PR Health Review* 1927; 2 (8): 9-12.

called tetanus) and writer's cramp (of the forearm and hand).[173] In contrast, the patients on the island often suffered from blood and bone marrow changes, a rare feature in sprue patients in Asia.[174] O'Connor saw cases on his visits to Presbyterian Hospital and noted that some of them might instead be suffering from pernicious anemia.[175] The question was clinically and scientifically important.[176] A mistaken diagnosis would deprive the patient of a speedy cure, because a treatment for pernicious anemia had just been developed in Boston—liver extract (the specific curative component was later identified as vitamin B_{12}).[177]

After these developments, the study of anemia became an even more exciting research field in Puerto Rico, where another causal factor (hookworm infection) was prevalent. A 1931 Rockefeller-sponsored commission for

173   Pérez-Santiago, Enrique and Butterworth Jr., Charles E. "Definition and diagnosis of sprue." *Am J Dig Dis* 1957; 2: 225-235.

174   Gardner, Frank H. "A malabsorption syndrome in military personnel in Puerto Rico." *AMA Archives of Internal Medicine* 1956; 98: 44-60.

175   O'Connor. *Diary...* (November 2).

176   Suárez, Jenaro. "Pernicious anemia and sprue." *PR Journal of Public Health and Tropical Medicine* 1931; 7: 145-165; and Ashford, Bailey K. "The differential diagnosis of sprue and pernicious anemia." *Am J Trop Med* 1932; 12: 199-215.

177   Keith Wailoo, K. *Drawing blood: technology and disease identity in twentieth-century America.* Baltimore: Johns Hopkins University Press, 1997: 118-122.

the clinical study of anemia[178] conducted clinical research at Presbyterian Hospital under the direction of renowned Harvard

---

178   The Rockefeller Anemia Commission is principally remembered in Puerto Rico in connection with its pathologist, Dr. Cornelius P. Rhoads. He wrote a personal letter (which he left at a secretary's desk) telling a Boston friend that "what the island needs is…something to totally exterminate the population…I have done my best to further the process of extermination by killing off 8 and transplanting cancer into several more." (Aponte Vázquez, Pedro I. *The unsolved case of Dr. Cornelius P. Rhoads: an indictment*. San Juan: Publicaciones René, 2005: 23-24.) The incoherent letter went on to lament the treatment that local doctors gave their patients. Rhoads later claimed it was all a joke, but before the letter was published in newspapers, he abruptly left for New York. The "joke" did not affect his career, but seventy years later, at the request of Puerto Rican academics and politicians, the American Association for Cancer Research removed Rhoads's name from a prestigious award to young researchers. (Wintrobe, M.M. *Hematology,* op. cit.: 514-515; Starr, Douglas. "Revisiting a 1930s scandal, AACR to rename a prize." *Science* 2003; 300: 573.) The letter provoked general indignation in Puerto Rico, and the episode received broad coverage locally, on the mainland, and internationally. (The scandal may have resulted in the choice of Puerto Rico as the fictional setting for *La Habanera*, a German Nazi-era film, 1937, that depicts a disease-ridden island with abusive public health authorities and a failed "Lambert Commission" from the Rockefeller Institute.) Official investigations by the government of Puerto Rico and the Rockefeller Foundation did not identify any suspicious deaths among his patients, but their methods were clearly partial to Rhoads. Aponte-Vázquez, who has published on this incident since 1982, is convinced that Rhoads's letter is a truthful confession, and highlights the many irregularities of the government's investigation, including the suppression of a second incriminating letter by Rhoads, the limited scope of the interrogatories (none of the stateside Commission staff was examined under oath and no fatal case was exhumed), and the obvious conflicts of interest of the physicians who assisted in ascertaining the facts Other historians have chosen to accept Rhoad's explanation as a "joke," although a malignant one, in the context of a racist environment for research on peoples of color and Rhoad's later involvement in experiments that exposed American troops to cancer-inducing chemicals without their knowledge. (Farley, J. *Rockefeller*, op.cit.: 80-82, 191-192; Lederer, S.E. "Porto Ricochet…," op. cit.; Bazell, Robert. "Growth industry." *The New Republic*, March 15, 1993: 13-14; Briggs, Laura. *Reproducing Empire: Race, sex, science, and U.S. imperialism in Puerto Rico*. Berkeley, CA: University of California Press, 2002: 67-77.)

hematologist William B. Castle.[179] Although this research was credited with demonstrating the lifesaving effectiveness of injected liver extract in advanced cases of sprue,[180] this had been at least suggested, if not proven, by Ashford in a small study published in 1928.[181] The ultimate cause of sprue remains unknown, but is suspected to be infectious. Researchers at the School of Tropical Medicine and its successor, the University of Puerto Rico School of Medicine, on their own and in different institutional collaborations, continued work on the problem for another three decades, achieving a better understanding of the intestinal abnormalities caused by the disease and the development of a successful treatment with antibiotics, folate, and B_{12} supplementation of the diet.[182]

---

179   Rhoads, C.P., Castle, W.B., Payne, G.C. and Lawson, H.A. "Observations on the etiology and treatment of anemia associated with hookworm infection in Puerto Rico." *Medicine* (New York Academy of Medicine) 1934; 13: 317-375.

180   Castle, William B. and Rhoads, Cornelius P. "Observations on the etiology and treatment of sprue in Puerto Rico [Abstract of presentation, plus transcript of discussion]." *Tr Assn Am Physicians* 1932; 47: 245–247. Abstract also printed in Clinical and Laboratory Notes, *Lancet* 1932; 219: 1198-1199. Wintrobe, Maxwell M. *Hematology, the blossoming of a science: a story of inspiration and effort.* Philadelphia: Lea & Febiger, 1985: 216.

181   Ashford, Bailey K. "Liver extract in the treatment of the anemia of sprue." *PR Journal of Public Health and Tropical Medicine* 1928; 4: 78-80.

182   Spies, Tom D., Suárez, Ramón M., Suárez Jr., Ramón M., Hernández Morales, Federico. "The therapeutic effect of folic acid in tropical sprue." *Science* 1946; 104: 75-76; Spies, Tom D., Suárez, Ramón M. "Response of tropical sprue to vitamin B12." *Blood* 1948; 3: 1213-1220. Suárez, Ramón M. "El pasado, el presente y el futuro del espru en Puerto Rico." *Bol Asoc Med P Rico* 1960; 52: 1-22; Crosby, William H. ed. *Tropical sprue: studies of the U.S. Army's sprue team in Puerto Rico.* Washington, D.C.: Walter Reed Army Institute of Research, Walter Reed Army Medical Center, Medical Science Publication no. 5 [1958]; Maldonado, Norman. "Tropical sprue—revisited." *PR Health Sci J* 1992; 11: 7-11.

Although a parasitologist, O'Connor was interested in all causes of death in Puerto Rico, even the non-infectious. Lambert, while conducting an autopsy on a man who took his own life, explained that suicides were common[183] and Commissioner Ortiz mentioned that murder was infrequent.[184] Indeed, the Vital Statistics Report for 1925-1926 noted no deaths due to homicide and 115 attributed to suicide.[185] In the more accurate data for 1931, there are 160 homicides and 313 suicides (10.1 and 19.8 per 100,000 population, respectively). The death rate from suicide in Puerto Rico has fluctuated around 10 per 100,000 since 1958, but homicide has been more frequent than suicide only since 1971. Homicide incidence peaked in 1993 at 26.8 and was 19.6 for 2001.[186] The ingestion of corrosive sublimate (mercury bichloride, a treatment for many conditions, including syphilis) was perhaps the most frequent method of suicide among the fatalities referred to Lambert for autopsy, but the predominant mode among suicides on the island was hanging.[187]

A rare cause of death that captured O'Connor's attention was shark attacks. His hosts at dinner on the first day of his visit "politely" turned the conversation to "matters other than medical," namely, gruesome accounts

---

183   O'Connor. *Diary...* (October 31).

184   O'Connor. *Diary...* (November 2).

185   Commissioner of Health of Porto Rico. *Report for Fiscal Year ending June 30, 1926*; 183-190.

186   Departamento de Salud de Puerto Rico. *Informe anual de estadísticas vitales 1977*. San Juan: Departamento de Salud, n.d.: 75; and Departamento de Salud de Puerto Rico. *Informe anual de estadísticas vitales, 2001*. San Juan: Departamento de Salud, 2003: 167.

187   Commissioner of Health of Porto Rico. *Report for Fiscal Year ending June 30, 1926*; 183-190.

of recent assaults by man-eating fish. As a result, the visiting parasitologist decided to forego sea bathing, and even at his farewell picnic, firmly on land, he watched, at a distance, "the fins of patrolling sharks."[188] While O'Connor was being frightened by these anecdotes at an exclusive club in San Juan, laborers in the south coast may have been dancing to a new tune that told the story of "lawyer Naegles" (*sic*, Neagle). Some of the Puerto Rican physicians may even have heard the piece, still remembered today for reasons unstated in O'Connor's account. In 1924, sugar corporations took the Puerto Rico government to federal court in an attempt to invalidate the government's appraisal of the 1920 earnings of the Guánica sugar mill ("Central"), one of the largest in the world.[189] This turned into a prolonged legal battle, because the amounts under discussion were not trivial.[190] Federal judge Odlin proposed that companies deposit a bond of nearly $900,000 in case they lost their suit.[191] This was almost enough to cover the Department of Health's budget for that year ($1,259,000).[192]

---

188   O'Connor. *Diary...* (November 13).

189   "El sensacional 'affaire' de la Guánica Central en la Corte Federal de Puerto Rico." *La Democracia*, 8 October 1925: 1, 5; and "El pleito de la Guánica Central contra el Tesorero de Puerto Rico." *La Correspondencia de Puerto Rico*, 9 October 1925: 1, 8.

190   Ramos, María E. *La muerte de un gigante. Historia de la Central Guánica y el poblado de Ensenada.* San Juan: Plaza Mayor, 1999: 126; and Ayala, C. *American Sugar*, op.cit.: 117-119.

191   "Una fianza de cerca de un millón de dólares tendrá que prestar ante la Corte Federal la Guánica Central para responder al Pueblo de P.R. de las contribuciones caso de que pierda el pleito." *El Mundo*, 6 June 1924: 3, 5.

192   Legislature of Porto Rico. *Acts and resolutions of the second session of the tenth Legislature of Porto Rico*. San Juan: Bureau of Supplies, Printing and Transportation, 1923: 358. (Act 50, Appropriations for the Government of Porto Rico for fiscal years ending June 30 1924 and June 30 1925, pages 272-378.)

Francis E. Neagle (1884-1968), a New York lawyer specialized in corporate law, was Guánica Central's attorney. He was hospitalized in critical condition at Presbyterian Hospital following a shark attack, but recovered.[193] His encounter with the shark became immortalized in song, a *plena* titled "Tintorera del mar," ("Lemon shark of the sea," *Negaprion brevirostris*). The *plena* is a fast-moving Afro-Puerto Rican dance form, developed on the southern coast of the island in the communities of sugarcane plantation workers at the turn of the nineteenth to the twentieth centuries. Its lyrics frequently chronicled a notable event (a fire, a crime, a railroad accident).[194] "Tintorera del mar" was neither a warning for swimmers. Instead, the incident became a political metaphor of how aggressive natives could outsmart powerful outsiders. The song's refrain that the shark "ate a lawyer of Guánica Central" was taken up by dancers celebrating the victory of laborers over the oppressive sugar *central*.[195]

---

193   Harvard University and Harvard Law School Alumni Archives; "Un tiburón en la playa del Condado atacó ayer a un prominente abogado continental." *La Correspondencia de Puerto Rico*, 8 October 1925: 1, 2; and "La tragedia de anteayer en el Parque Borinquen." *El Mundo*, 9 October 1925: 1, 6.

194   Glasser, Ruth. *My music is my flag: Puerto Rican musicians and their New York communities, 1917-1940.* Berkeley, CA: University of California Press, 1995: 171-177.

195   "Tintorera del mar,/ tintorera del mar,/ tintorera del mar,/ se comió un abogado de la Guánica Central." Words and music by Manuel Jiménez ("Canario"), copyright 1978 by Peer International Corporation, New York. The melody is written out in Lorenzo Homar's woodcut, "Tintorera del mar," see: http://www.atelier-rc.com/Atelier.RC/ LHomar.html (accessed 5 November 2006). See also Aponte Ledée, Rafael. "María la de Utuado: Los orígenes de la plena, segunda parte." *El Nuevo Día*, Revista Domingo, San Juan, 25 April 1999: 18-19, and Ayoroa Santaliz, José Enrique. *De serenata.* San Juan: Eds. Huracán, 2000: 15-34.

Conclusion

The government of Puerto Rico eventually lost its suit against the sugar corporations, but the workers' hope was fulfilled in even broader terms.[196] Within 20 years (1947), the overall mortality rate in Puerto Rico declined from 20.6 to 12 deaths per thousand population, infant mortality fell from 151 to 71.5 deaths per thousand live births, and life expectancy at birth rose from under 40 to almost 60 years.[197] All these improvements were the result of public health measures, scientific developments (especially the discovery of antibiotics), economic advancements, and global as well as local political upheavals. Depression-era food relief, World War II, the Popular Democratic Party's social legislation, and the beginning of industrialization had a great impact on health in Puerto Rico.

O'Connor ends his diary with a forecast that "before long Porto Rico should make valuable contributions to medicine,"[198] and his prediction was proven right. From the late 1920s to the 1940s, Puerto Rico's research and educational institutions, and its long-suffering and collaborative population, carried out a multitude of studies on the nature, impact, and prevention of common and obscure diseases

---

196   Ayala, C. *American Sugar*, op.cit.: 117-119.
197   Costa Mandry, O. *Apuntes*, op. cit.: 106-107; and Departamento de Salud de Puerto Rico. *Informe anual de estadísticas vitales 1972*. San Juan: Departamento de Salud, n.d.: 4.
198   O'Connor. *Diary...* (November 21).

(only a small fraction of which have been referenced here).[199]

Puerto Rico is at present the world's fifth largest manufacturer of pharmaceutical products (64% of all island exports in 2004).[200] Sugarcane plantations are gone. Puerto Ricans are in the midst of an obesity epidemic, and the principal causes of death are cancer, cardiovascular diseases, and other chronic conditions.[201] Most of the institutions O'Connor visited have disappeared. The Tuberculosis Sanatorium was replaced by a conglomerate of tertiary care specialty hospitals, the present Puerto Rico Medical Center.

---

199   This review has focused on the work performed by Francis O'Connor and his colleagues. Perforce it leaves out two of the most original, enterprising, and independent physicians in Puerto Rico in the twentieth century, who were O'Connor's contemporaries, Isaac González Martínez (1871-1954) and Pedro Gutiérrez Igaravídez (1871-1935). Also, some of the young physicians mentioned briefly in the diary, such as Ramón M. Suárez (1895-1981), Oscar Costa Mandry (1898-1991), and Enrique Koppisch (1904-1961) later developed clinical and research careers that gained them international recognition, but their contributions are not covered here. See: Anon. "El Dr. Gutiérrez Igaravídez define su actitud en el asunto de la 'Escuela de Medicina Tropical.'" *El Mundo*, 2 May 1927: 1, 12, 13. Torregrosa, Arturo. "En la muerte de un gran puertorriqueño [Gutiérrez]." [Revista] *Puerto Rico* 1935; 1 (3): 208-215. Pacheco Padró, Antonio. *Isaac González Martínez, su vida y su obra*. Ciudad Trujillo [Santo Domingo]: Ed. Montalvo, 1954. Torres Gómez, José M., and García Palmieri, Mario R. eds. (Memorial issue in honor of Dr. Ramón M. Suárez) *Bol Asoc Med P Rico* 1983; 75 (11). Maldonado, Norman. "Enrique Koppisch and his legacy." *The San Juan Star*, August 19, 2003: 59. Pérez Santiago, Enrique. "Homenaje póstumo a Dr. Oscar Costa Mandry." *Prensa Médica* (Asociación Médica de Puerto Rico) 1994; 6 (4): 14, 19.

200   Villamil, José J. ed. *Puerto Rico 2025: una nueva visión para el futuro de Puerto Rico*. San Juan: Comité Timón Puerto Rico 2025, 2004: 18; and Martínez, Marialba. "Global pharmaceutical-drug sales in 2005 for 9 local companies up 5.7% to 102.5 billion." *Caribbean Business* [San Juan] 18 August 2005: 30-31. See also: Pharmaceutical Industry Association website, www.piapr.com (accessed 4 November 2006).

201   Parés Arroyo, Marga. "Epidémica en la Isla la obesidad. Tendencia peligrosa para la salud." *El Nuevo Día*, San Juan, 19 October 2005: 1, 4-5.

The School of Tropical Medicine was closed, to be transmuted into the University of Puerto Rico School of Medicine, now also sited at the Medical Center. The Leprosarium, long a ruin, recently underwent a partial remodeling. The women's section has been converted into a residential treatment facility for mental health patients. The Psychiatric Hospital is still open, although it is no longer the only hospital on the island for treating mental illness.

From the example of Puerto Rico, one may argue that the discipline of tropical medicine was not only useful to maintain the labor force, but was further made necessary by the social and ecologic impact of exploitative agricultural development. Economic growth could be demonstrated by commerce and labor statistics, but as historian César Ayala has indicated, in this "development of underdevelopment" the mass of society became a landless, malnourished proletariat.[202] It is likely that man-made changes in the environment contributed to the exacerbation of diseases. The high-intensity foci of malaria and schistosomiasis coincided with the location of the largest sugarcane plantations, south of a diagonal drawn from the southwest corner to the northeast corner of Puerto Rico.[203] Although irrigation projects could transform a desert into a garden, the water channels became a motor for the expansion of infectious agents in the population.[204] The garden benefited

---

202   Ayala, C. *American Sugar,* op. cit.: 3, 247.

203   Ibid.: 223-225.

204   In India, irrigation canals and railway embankments also expanded the habitats of malaria mosquitoes. See: I. Klein. Malaria and mortality in Bengal, 1840-1921. *Indian Economic and Social History Review* 1972; 9: 132-160. The cultivation and commerce of sugar cane has also been associated with the spread of yellow fever; see: J.D. Goodyear, "The sugar connection: a new perspective on the history of yellow fever." *Bulletin of the History of Medicine* 1978; 52: 5-21.

the corporation; the diseases affected the workers.[205] Indeed, after improvements in the first decade of the century, the general mortality rate in Puerto Rico remained unchanged for about 30 years (near 20 per thousand population from 1908 to 1937, with some tragic years of marked increase) despite of all clinical and public health efforts.[206]

Then, in ten years, mortality was cut in half (from 20 to 10 per thousand).[207] Can the disappearance of endemic scourges also be attributed to environmental change? It is tempting to ascribe the elimination of malaria to the vast effort in draining mosquito habitats, but Luis Palacios, former director of the Malaria Control Bureau, judged that those activities had reduced mosquito exposure for only a small proportion of the population. He attributed the decrease in malaria incidence to an intensified treatment program with quinine, which interrupted the chain of transmission.[208] That type of intervention seems to have not been effective in the southern United States; moreover, it fails to explain the disappearance of filaria, for which there was no antiparasitic medication.[209] Clearly the drainage and "DDTzation" efforts reduced mosquito populations. But broader societal forces

---

205   Again, Emilio S. Belaval (*Cuentos para fomentar el turismo*, op. cit.: p. 69) presents an unforgettable image of the problem. In his story "Mantengo" (Welfare), an old farm laborer, shivering and hallucinating with fever in a hut on a rocky hillside, wants to wrap himself in a tip of the green blanket that covers the valley beneath, but he isn't strong enough to pry it loose from the barbed wire with which the "central" has surrounded it.

206   Pérez, Manuel A. "Factors contributing to a high death rate in Puerto Rico". *PR Journal of Public Health and Tropical Medicine* 1933; 8: 421-447.

207   Vázquez Calzada, José Luis. "El descenso de la mortalidad en Puerto Rico: un hecho histórico notable." *PR Health Sci J* 1984; 3: 173-181.

208   Palacios, L. *Informe,* op. cit.: 304-305.

209   Humphreys, M. *Malaria*, op. cit.: 75-79.

were also at work. As incomes rose, nutritional and housing conditions improved, and electricity, water, and sewer services reached rural areas, the population's exposure to mosquitoes and contaminated soil and water decreased. As a result, the Puerto Rican's individual and collective immunity was strengthened. The emergence and disappearance of schistosomiasis is even more difficult to attribute to a single cause, in part because statistics are less directly related to disease activity. The peak in bilharzia reporting, in the 1950s, may have been due to the Control Program's activities, but it could also have been a true peak, produced years after the infection occurred, that may be ascribed to the lag between infection and appearance of liver involvement.[210] In contrast to malaria, filaria, and schistosomiasis, leprosy and sprue seem to currently maintain their secular rate of low prevalence.

This epochal change indicates that the scientific and institutional achievements O'Connor described were set in a more unstable social situation than he could perceive or the diary reveal. O'Connor's account of programs or situations was not correct in all details, which is hardly surprising. No short-term traveler can be a perfectly reliable chronicler in a new country. The present-day reader must nevertheless acknowledge the diarist's acuteness in description, not only for the more important aspects of activities he understood, but for what he saw, heard, and sensed.

---

210 In addition, one could hypothesize that, because the disease's most severe complications occur when the body produces a strong immune defense, it was not until the population was better nourished that the prevalence of those symptoms increased.

Travel Writing:
Close Encounters through Discerning Eyes

Silvia E. Rabionet

rancis O'Connor's *Diary of a Porto Rican Trip* exemplifies
many features of the genre of travel literature,
characterized by the sharing of the "I" and the "eye"
of travelers as they visit new places. Through daily entries,
O'Connor presents a unique view of the island's health
conditions and public health system, while participating
as a visiting lecturer and scientist at the School of Tropical
Medicine. He records and comments upon the academic and
scientific activities in which he was involved for approximately
a month in the year 1927. His observations are accompanied by
candid descriptions of the tropical surroundings which enthrall
him while visiting health facilities and programs throughout
the country. O'Connor's diary provokes our curiosity and
transports us back into Puerto Rico's health history. It invites
us to reflect upon the observer and the observed, when two
cultures come into close encounter through the discerning
eyes of an avid scientist.

The travel narrative has a long, notable, and evolving history. As a literary genre, it encompasses a wide range of works whose main purpose is to share the observations of places foreign to the writer. It is a "varied body of writing that takes travel as an essential condition for its production, that... is best defined by its plurality."[1] Travel writings appear in many forms, including memoirs, journals, personal diaries, ships' logs, letters, essays, autobiographies, and even poems. They comprise narratives and stories of adventure, exploration, journeys, displacement, and exile. Travel literature—whether inspired by pleasure, pilgrimage, official duty, geographical exploration, or profit—emerges as a significant genre in all times and cultures.[2]

Travel accounts often tell us as much about the author as of the subject matter. They are therefore doubly valuable as sources for in depth cultural and historical exploration. As historical documents, they pose the question of authenticity inherent in the tension between objective and subjective reporting.[3] Nevertheless, travel accounts constitute a valuable primary source for historians because they provide information about details of daily lives and events not recorded in other sources. Particularly reflective travelers, like Francis O'Connor, offer novel insights into the societies they visit. Furthermore, their accounts express their values and experiences, reflecting

1   Rubiés, Joan Pau. "Travel writing and ethnography." In Peter Hulme and Tim Youngs, eds. *The Cambridge Companion to Travel Writing*. England: Cambridge University Press, 2002: 242-260; 244.

2   Bassnett, Susan. "Introduction." In Jennifer Speake, ed. *Literature of Travel and Exploration: An Encyclopedia*. Volume I. New York: Routledge, 2003: *xi-xv*; *xi*.

3   Blanton, Casey. *Travel Writing*. New York: Routledge, 1995: *xi*.

the interests and concerns of their own societies during the period in which the journey took place.

The writers' involvement with the foreign is not limited to places; it also includes observations of persons, morals, cultures, and events. Most narratives are told in the first person using a journey pattern: departure, adventure, and return.[4] Beyond this simple structure lies a wealth of descriptions and interpretations of places, people, and events mediated by the knowledge, purpose, intention, and ability of the traveler to engage and link his inner self and the outer world.[5] Often, the eye is less important than the "I": the traveler/writer sees and experiences places and events from a particular, idiosyncratic perspective.

Throughout the centuries, readers have been fascinated by travel accounts. Early forms of the genre date to the beginning of fiction writing itself. Indeed, one of the very earliest travel stories was composed in Egypt during the Twelfth Dynasty.[6] Epic sagas such as Homer's *Odyssey* and biblical accounts like the *Exodus* are examples of early texts whose titles have become synonymous with adventurous and difficult journeys.[7] Other examples of the genre in the ancient world include Herodotus's *History of the Persian Wars* (440 B.C.E.), which narrates the writer's expeditions in Egypt and Anatolia; Strabo's *Geographica* (*ca.* 23 C.E.); and Pausanias's

---

4   Ibid.: 2-3.

5   Ibid.

6   Hulme, Peter and Youngs, Tim. "Introduction." *The Cambridge Companion to Travel Writing*, op.cit.: 1-16; 2.

7   Ibid.

Guide to Greece, (*ca.* 170 C.E). All provide information about geography and customs deemed different and exotic by the writers.[8]

During the Middle Ages, pilgrims, crusaders, missionaries, and merchants traveled widely and left numerous travel accounts in the form of poems, letters, music, and pilgrimage maps. Egeria's *Peregrinatio ad terram sanctam* (Pilgrimage to the Holy Land; *ca.* 500 C.E.), constitutes the first account of the Christian quest for the Holy Land. Egeria, a fifth century Christian nun, narrates her journey to the Holy Land in letter form, using the first person.[9] Such pilgrimages became a devotional and touristic experience throughout the Middle Ages. As a result, travel guides for pilgrimages or religious quests emerged as a popular form of travel writing.

In the late seventh century, Bishop Arculfus of Gaul was shipwrecked off Scotland on his return from the Holy Land, where he had spent nine months visiting Jerusalem, Bethlehem, Nazareth, the Dead Sea, and the Sea of Galilee, among other places. After extending his travels as far as Tyre and Damascus, he sailed to Alexandria, taking forty days to accomplish the voyage. From Egypt he went to Crete and Constantinople. On his homeward voyage, he visited Sicily and proceeded to Rome. After leaving Rome his ship was caught in a violent storm which drove it completely off course, finally docking in Scotland. In Scotland, he stayed with Adamnan, the abbot of the island monastery of Iona.

---

8   Blanton, C., *Travel Writing*, op. cit.: 1-2.
9   The first-person narration will later become a defining characteristic of the genre. Ra' ad, Basem, L. "Teaching Travel in the Eastern Mediterranean." Unpublished manuscript. Al Quds University, Jerusalem, 1995: 6-7.

During his stay, the Bishop related his journey and Adamnan wrote it in three volumes titled *De locis sanctis* (Of Holy Places; 670 C.E.). This was the first guide for pilgrims to the Holy Land.[10]

In the late Middle Ages, Marco Polo's descriptions of his travels across Asia marked a shift in travel writing. The traditional religious narrative which characterized pilgrimage and crusade accounts was replaced by mundane and realistic descriptions of the East. Marco Polo's *The Travels* provided practical information concerning geography, routes, people, and laws. Although serious questions of authenticity and accuracy have been raised about this text, no one doubts its importance as a source of inspiration for other travelers and merchants.[11] In the early fourteenth century, Friar Oderic of Pordenone[12] embarked on a similar journey across Asia accompanied by several other monks. He produced an equally interesting text, *Itinerarius* (Itinerary; *ca.* 1330 C.E.).[13] The most popular travel account of the period was *The Travels of Sir John Mandeville,* narrated by a probably fictional fourteenth century English knight. This text is considered a plagiarized compendium of previously written accounts and materials describing Arabia, Central Asia, North Africa, and the Far East, including some

---

10   Macpherson, James Rose, "Preface." In *The Pilgrimage of Arculfus in the Holy Land (Translation).* London, 1895; and Smethurst, Paul. "English 2045-Travel Writings, course notes." University of Hong Kong, English Department, 2000.

11   Hulme, P. and Youngs, T. "Introduction," op. cit.: 3.

12   Also know as Oderic of Portenau.

13   Kerr, Robert. "Travel of Oderic of Portenau, into China and the East, in 1318. (Introduction)." *A General History and Collection of Voyages and Travels, 1.* 1811: Ch. XII. (Online version by Explorion http: explorion.net.); and Bassnett, S. "Introduction," op. cit.: *xii.*

of Oderic's texts. Its popularity is primarily attributed to the narrator's ability to engage the reader through humor, irony, and political and philosophical insights.[14]

Events that define distinct historical periods and movements (e.g., the Age of Discovery and Exploration, the Renaissance, Romanticism, Industrialization, the World Wars, etc.) provide the context for major milestones in the characterization and permanence of travel writing in its modern form. At the same time, these events mark an evolution of the travelers' portrayal of the foreign and of their perception of the foreign.[15] In Europe and America, the modern development of the genre can be traced by examining the role that travelers assumed as they encountered the foreign.

Modern travel literature begins in the late fifteenth century with the accounts of Christopher Columbus. As in earlier periods, this form of storytelling evoked curiosity and seduced readers. The discovery of the New World had an aura of mystery and created a need to explain the "new" geography and peoples. It awakened ideas and promises of coming across the novel, the exotic, or the extreme. Coinciding with the expansion of colonial Europe to the south and the east, the four voyages of Columbus (1492-93, 1493-96, 1498-1500 and 1502-04) led the way for the exploration and colonization of the Americas.[16]

Columbus included a great deal of travel reporting in the log of his first voyage to the western hemisphere—which itself survives only in a later historical account composed by

---

14   Ra' ad, Basem, L. "Teaching Travel…," op.cit.: 8-9.

15   Blanton, C. *Travel Writing*, op.cit.: 7-29.

16   Whitehead, Neil L. "South America/Amazonia: the forest of marvels." *The Cambridge Companion to Travel Writing*, op.cit.: 122-138; 122.

the Spanish missionary Fray Bartolomé de las Casas. He also wrote three letters[17] addressed to his patrons, King Ferdinand and Queen Isabella, and to other royal officials. In his travel narratives, Christopher Columbus claimed ownership over the land and the people. He seemed overwhelmed by the landscape and the exotic nature of its inhabitants. He was not only recording his feats but also reporting to his sponsors, quite literally accounting for resources expended and outcomes achieved:[18]

> [Sunday December 16, 1492]
>
> Be sure that this island and all the others are as much your own as is Castile, for all that is needed here is a seat of government and to command them to do what you wish, for I with these people I have with me, who are not many, could travel throughout these islands unopposed, and I have seen three of these sailors go ashore alone where there was a crowd of these Indians, and they have all run off, without anyone wishing them any harm. They have no weapons and are all naked and with no experience of arms and very timid, so that a thousand of them would not stand up to three of us, and so they are suitable to take

---

17   The term "Columbus's letter" usually refers to one of the fifteenth-century printed editions of a letter from his first voyage announcing his "discovery" of America. A traditional view holds that Columbus wrote three letters: one addressed to Luis de Santangel, Keeper of Accounts of Aragon, dated February 15th, 1493; a second addressed to King Ferdinand and Queen Isabella, of which no copy has survived; and a third sent to Gabriel Sanchez, Treasurer of Aragon, dated March 15th, 1493. Recent thinking on the subject is that all three letters were derived from a single manuscript sent to Ferdinand and Isabella from which copies were then made and endorsed to several court officials. (New York Public Library, Research Guide: *Christopher Columbus and Early European Exploration*)

18   Blanton, C. *Travel Writing*, op. cit.: 9.

orders and be made to work, sow and do anything else that may be needed, and build towns and be taught to wear clothes and adopt our customs.[19]

Columbus's writings represented yet another shift in travel writing: his logs were accounts of journeys and places in which the traveler was protagonist. Following Columbus, conquering heroes became prominent as European ships traveled around the world in search of new trading routes to expand commerce. In their accounts, which date from the late fifteenth century to the end of the sixteenth century, travelers appeared as romantic heroes leading the reader through the "discovered" lands, in search of riches, motivated by ambition and bountiful earnings.[20] While expressing their views about the exotic, they highlighted grandiose discoveries worth additional support by sponsors. They also illustrated the strong connection between religion and colonization.[21]

One of the major sources for the early history of the New World is Pietro Martire d' Anghiera's *Decades*. The first edition appeared in 1511, and three expanded editions were subsequently published in 1530 and 1532. The *Decades*, later translated and published in Italy, France, Germany and England, consists of compilations of reports and documents describing

---

19   Columbus, Christopher. *The Diary of Christopher Columbus's First Voyage to America, 1492-1493*, abstracted by Fray Bartolomé de las Casas. Oliver Dunn and James E. Kelley, Jr., trans. Norman: University of Oklahoma Press, 1989.

20   Franklin, Wayne. *Discoverers, Explorers, Settlers: Diligent Writers of Early America*. Chicago: The University of Chicago Press, 1979: 1-21.

21   Acosta, José de. *Natural and Moral History of the Indies (1590)*. Jane E. Mangan, ed. Francis M. Lopes-Moralles. Trans. Durham: Duke University Press, 2002.

the initial voyages to the New World.[22] As a royal historian to the Spanish court, d' Anghiera obtained information directly from travel narratives and accounts provided by Columbus, Cortés, Vasco da Gama, and other explorers and conquerors, as well as from memoranda and reports submitted to the king.[23] It should be noted that although Puerto Rico was discovered in 1493 on Columbus' second voyage and settled before the end of the sixteenth century, it does not figure prominently in the accounts of American voyages and travels of the time. It received only minor mention from Las Casas, Pietro Martire d' Anghiera, and other early historiographers. The first significant work devoted to Puerto Rico was the *Historia Geográfica, Civil y Natural* published in the eighteenth century by Fray Iñigo Abbad y Lasierra.[24]

The centrality of the narrator is also present in travel writings by Sir Walter Raleigh, who has been regarded as one of the most accomplished travel writers of the Renaissance. The English explorer ventured into South America in 1595, visiting the lower Orinoco River in search for the mythical El Dorado.[25] Raleigh's account, *The Discoverie of the Large, Rich, and Bewtiful Empyre of Guiana* (1596), is distinguished by "its unprecedented attention to geographic and ethnographic details and its autobiographical strategies, which projected a sense of

---

22   Sherman, William H. "Stirrings and searchings (1500-1720)." *The Cambridge Companion to Travel Writing*, op.cit.: 17-36; 19.

23   Anghiera, Pietro Martire d'. *The Decades of the Newe Worlde or West India.* Facsimile reprint of the 1555 ed. pub. London: Guilhelmi Powell, trans. Richard Eden. March of America Facsimile Series, no. 4. Ann Arbor: University Microfilms, 1966.

24   Ober, Fredrick. *Puerto Rico and its Resources,* 1899. Reprinted in 2005 by Fundación Puertorriqueña de la Humanidades (We the People Puerto Rico Collection).

25   Blanton, C. *Travel Writing*, op. cit.: 10.

heroism onto the otherwise unsuccessful venture,…allowed to explore not only exotic others but the English selves that came into contact with them."[26] During this period, explorers and colonizers were not the only ones leaving written accounts. Pilgrims, merchants, ambassadors, scientists, captives and castaways contributed with important narrations in which the travelers made foreign experiences available to readers. Faced with the challenge of narrating the facts and observations, these travelers recorded their process of "self-understanding as an essential way in shaping their lives after the fact."[27]

The publication of two English collections of travel writings and anthologies during the Age of Discovery and Exploration were significant contributions to the genre. Richard Hakluyt's *The Principal Navigators, Voyages, Traffiques, and Discoveries of the English Nation*, published in 1589, and Samuel Purchas's *Hakluytus Posthmus or Purchas His Pilgrimes*, published in 1625, were multi-volume catalogued collections documenting England's maritime expansion, while preserving original logs, maps, and itineraries. The editorial comments provide religious, social, and economic interpretations on samples of the genre, illustrating their significance as a source of cultural information.[28] These anthologies ignite and facilitate the enjoyment and study of travel by recognizing "that the real power of travel writing lay in its independence of perspective."[29]

By the seventeenth century, travel literature cemented

---

26   Sherman, W.H. "Stirrings and searchings…," op. cit.: 26.

27   Franklin, Wayne. *Discoverers, Explorers, Settlers: Diligent Writers of Early America.* Chicago: The University of Chicago Press, 1979: 2.

28   Ibid.: 22.

29   Hulme, P. and Youngs, T. "Introduction," op. cit.: 4.

its importance as a genre by becoming a valuable source of knowledge for the discipline of *natural philosophy* or the objective study of nature and the physical world. Sir Francis Bacon, Purchas's contemporary and the most influential English essayist and philosopher of science of the time, drew attention to the significance of travel accounts for the understanding of natural histories.[30] His work *Of Travel* (1625) emphasized the link between traveling and education: "Travel, in the younger sort, is a part of education, in the elder, a part of experience. He that travelleth into a country…goeth to school, and not to travel."[31] He encouraged travelers to keep diaries to systematically collect natural knowledge:

> Let diaries, therefore, be brought in use. The things to be seen and observed are: the courts of princes, especially when they give audience to ambassadors; the courts of justice, while they sit and hear causes; and so of consistories ecclesiastic; the churches and monasteries, with the monuments which are therein extant; the walls and fortifications of cities, and towns, and so the heavens and harbors; antiquities and ruins; libraries; colleges, disputations, and lectures, where any are; shipping and navies; houses and gardens of state and pleasure, near great cities; armories; arsenals; magazines; exchanges; burses; warehouses; exercises of horsemanship, fencing, training of soldiers, and the like; comedies, such whereunto the better sort of persons do resort;

---

30   Ibid.
31   Bacon, Francis, 1625. *Of Travel*   12 Jan. 2006. Francis Bacon Online, 18 Jan. 2008. <http:// www.westegg.com/bacon/travel.html>.

treasuries of jewels and robes; cabinets and rarities; and, to conclude, whatsoever is memorable, in the places where they go...[32]

The new paradigm of travel as a finishing school was known as the *Grand Tour*. The purpose of travel "was to round out the education of young men of the ruling classes by exposing them to the treasured artifacts and ennobling society of the Continent."[33] The eighteenth century witnessed the explosion of accounts of real and imaginary travels based on the Grand Tour. English gentlemen visited different parts of Continental Europe to acquire knowledge within a larger social and cultural context. "Through their interactions with their hosts, a recognition of different cultural values served as the basis for the self-fashioning of the larger number of English natural philosophers."[34] Travel reports and the writings of young Englishmen who had just finished their university degree set the stage for the scientific and philosophical revolutions that flourished in the eighteenth century. In fact, travel literature became so integrated with the interests of natural philosophers that extensive travel reports appeared

32   Ibid.

33   Buzard, James. "The Grand Tour and After (1660- 1840)." *The Cambridge Companion to Travel Writing*, op.cit.: 37-52; 38.

34   Illiffe, Robert. "Foreign Bodies: Travel, Empire and the Early Royal Society of London. Part II. The Land of Experimental Knowledge." *Canadian Journal of History* April 1999: 1-3. (Online version by ProQuest.)

consistently in the journal of The Royal Society of London,[35] the *Philosophical Transactions*,[36] well into the eighteenth century.[37] John Locke, founder of British empiricism and regarded as one of the most influential natural philosophers, drew upon his vast collection of travel accounts for his writings.[38]

Travel writers seemed to consciously use the external experience to explore internal feelings. The challenge of narrating from an autobiographical or scientific perspective reached new heights as works by Locke, Newton, and Rousseau influenced travelers. The various literary, scientific and philosophical works that coincided in the late seventeenth and the eighteenth century provided the context for the emergence of travelers who showed an increasing "entanglement between self and the world."[39]

But not all travel by young Englishmen was motivated by scientific or philosophical interests, nor did it produce accounts of scientific value. Laurence Sterne, in *A Sentimental Journey* (1768), recognized that during the period there were many kinds of travelers who were experiencing the Grand Tour

35   The origins of the Royal Society lie in an "invisible college" of natural philosophers who began meeting in the mid-1640s to discuss the ideas of Francis Bacon. At first apparently nameless, the name The Royal Society first appears in print in 1661, and in the second Royal Charter of 1663 the Society is referred to as "The Royal Society of London for Improving Natural Knowledge."

36   In 1665, the first issue of *Philosophical Transactions* was edited by the Royal Society's Secretary. The Society took over publication some years later and the journal is now the oldest scientific journal in continuous publication.

37   Illiffe, Robert. "Foreign Bodies: Travel, Empire and the Early Royal Society of London. Part 1 Englishmen on Tour." *Canadian Journal of History* Dec 1998: 1-3. (On-line version by ProQuest.); and Bridges, Roy. "Exploration and travel outside Europe (1720-1914). *The Cambridge Companion to Travel Writing*, op.cit.: 53-69; 56.

38   Hulme, P. and Youngs, T. "Introduction," op. cit.: 4.

39   Blanton, C. *Travel Writing,* op. cit.: 11.

in different ways: "idle travellers, inquisitive travellers, lying travellers, proud travellers, vain travellers, splenetic travellers."[40] Prominent travel narratives and texts from the eighteenth century include: Daniel Defoe's, *A Tour thro' the Whole Islands of Great Britain (1724-1726);* James Boswell's *Boswell on the Grand Tour: Italy, Corsica and France (1765-1766);* Tobias Smollet's *Travel through France and Italy (1766);* and Samuel Johnson's *A Journey to the Western Island of Scotland (1775).* In these texts, including Sterne's, renowned writers used the journey as material for writing and as a structural device for the narration. The use of travel by established writers would proliferate in the centuries to follow.

During the eighteenth century, women also emerged as important contributors to travel writing. The "female gaze" on the foreign started to acquire a meaningful status in travel literature.[41] Some women traveled abroad with appointed diplomats and had the opportunity to interact with foreign culture and women. Among the first and most notable modern travel writer was Lady Mary Wortley Montagu, the wife of a British ambassador who accompanied her husband to Ottoman Turkey from 1714 to 1718. A fearless traveler, she wrote extensively in the form of letters[42] about the impressions of her journeys and about Turkish women, including those in

---

40   Sterne, Laurence. *A Sentimental Journey through France and Italy, 1768.* Reprint, Berkley: University of California Press, 1967: 34-35. As cited by Blanton, C. *Travel Writing*, op. cit.: 14.

41   Lorcin, Patricia M.A. "Women's Travel Writing." In *World History Resources, George Mason University: Center for History and New Media,* 2003-2005. http://chmn. gmu.edu/worldhistorysources/.

42   The letters included in the collection. *Turkish Embassy Letters,* were written from 1716 to 1718, but were published posthumously in 1763.

the Turkish harem of the Sultan of Istanbul.[43] Her accounts portray Turkish women as "domesticated," in clear contrast with the lascivious and erotic characterization of women in accounts produced by male travelers, such as George Sandys (*A Relation of a Journey*, 1652) and Monsieur de Thevenot (*Relation d'un voyage fait au Levant*, 1665).[44]

The late eighteenth century and the nineteenth century are considered by many travel scholars as the heyday of travel writing and travel literature. The advent of Romanticism, allowing for the emotional expression and for the display of imagination, greatly influenced the traveling and the accounts that followed. Coinciding with the period, the Industrial Revolution led to advances in transportation (i.e., trains and steamships) which spurred travel. It also led to a great expansion of the middle classes and the possibility of traveling for pleasure.[45] During this period, voyages and explorations continued by sea and land. European explorers produced important travel texts as they continued to map and augment territories across the globe. As a result, the genre saw the consolidation of two well-defined and distinct strands of work: one of a more literary nature influenced by elements of the Romantic Era, and a second one responding to the growth of the European empires.[46] "Travel writing had clearly become a matter of self discovery as well as a record for the discovery of others."[47]

---

43   Bassnett, Susan. "Travel Writing and Gender." *The Cambridge Companion to Travel Writing*, op. cit.: 225-241; 229; and Pratt, Mary Louise. *Imperial Eyes: Travel Writing and Transculturation*. New York: Routdledge, 1992: 167-168.
44   Heffernan, Teresa. "Feminism against the East/West Divide: Lady Mary's Turkish Embassy Letters." *Eighteenth-Century Studies* 2000; 33 (2): 201-215.
45   Bassnett, S. "Introduction," op. cit.: *xiii-xiv*.
46   Bridges, R. "Exploration and travel…," op.cit.: 63-66.
47   Blanton, C. *Travel Writing*, op. cit.: 14

The Romantic travel writings of the nineteenth century retain many of the characteristics of the Grand Tour accounts, but at the same time they introduce an individual sensibility and sublime perspective on beauty.[48] Within this group of travel writers we find, as in the previous century, renowned writers who used the journey as material for writing. They can be considered more as writers who traveled, than travelers who wrote. Mark Twain, in the preface to *Innocents Abroad* (1869) reflects upon his approach to travel writing:

> I make small pretense of showing anyone how he ought to look at objects of interest beyond the sea—other books do that, and therefore, even if I were competent to do it, there is no need. I offer no apologies for any departures from the usual style of travel writing that may be charged against me—for I think I have seen with impartial eyes, and I am sure I have written at least honestly, whether wisely or not.[49]

Other contemporaries of Twain who produced travel narratives include Stendhal (*Memoirs of a Tourist,* 1838), Charles Dickens (*Pictures from Italy,* 1846 and *American Notes,* 1842), and Robert Louis Stevenson (*Travels with a Donkey in the Cévennes,* 1879 and *In the South Seas,* 1896). These professional writers contributed to the genre by providing well-crafted works of outstanding literary value.

Charles Darwin, well known for his scientific publications, belongs to the group of travel writers who

---

48   Leask, Nigel. *Curiosity and the Aesthetics of Travel Writing: 1770-1840.* London: Oxford University Press, 2004: 15-54.

49   Twain, Mark. *Innocents Abroad.* New York: Dover Publication, 2003 ed.: 1. (First published, 1869)

significantly contributed to the evolution of the genre during the nineteenth century. His book, *Narrative of the Surveying Voyages of His Majesty's Ships Adventure and Beagle* (1839), constitutes an excellent example of the intersection of science, sentiment, and "imperial gaze" encountering the foreign. Darwin presents a naturalist's record of a five-year scientific voyage as a very personal record of a man awakening to the huge possibilities on his horizon, both literally and figuratively. He is humbled by the spectacular landscapes of the coasts of South America, the Galapagos Islands, Tahiti, and Australia. At the same time, he suggests that England can bring moral improvement to the world and native cultures.[50] *Voyages* has been seminal in tracing and identifying the roots of Darwin's postulates on natural selection, upon which the modern theory of evolution is based. Natural selection is later explained in his book, *The Origin of Species* (1859), probably one of the most influential books of all times.[51]

The unprecedented growth of the British Empire between the late nineteenth century and the early twentieth century generated much travel literature linked to the expansion of the empire, especially in Africa, India, and the Americas. The writings of David Livingstone's *Missionary Travels and Researches in South Africa* (1857), Richard Burton's *Personal Narratives of Pilgrimage to Al-Madinah and Meccah* (1855), Lafcadio Hearn's *Two Years in the French West Indies* (1890) and *Glimpses of Unfamiliar Japan* (1894), and Mary Kingsley's *Travels in West Africa* (1897) are examples of accounts in which trade, diplomacy, missionary endeavor and scientific exploration

---

50   Blanton, C. *Travel Writing*, op. cit.: 9-20.
51   Ibid.

intermingle with the assumed intellectual supremacy of the Europeans, particularly the English during a period known as the "New Imperialism."[52] Notable within this period are the travel writings of Florence Nightingale, known for her pioneering contributions to nursing education and public health practices. Prior to devoting herself fully to her career, Florence Nightingale traveled widely through Europe and Egypt. From 1847 to 1853 she wrote multiple letters and kept detailed travel diaries that revealed her spiritual and intellectual development, as well as the roots of her ideas on social and health care reform.[53]

Like Darwin, Francis W. O'Connor was one of the many travelers that visited the "less developed" world for the benefit and expansion of science within the context of imperialism. He believed in "the potentiality of scientists, and especially of medical ones, to smash nationalism and eventually bring about good will amongst the various nationalities."[54] In his diary he argues that "in all countries scientists are doing more that anyone else to spread good feeling, but they are seriously handicapped by the political agents and by uneducated and ill-bred tourists."[55] There are many entries in Francis

---

52   Bridges, R. "Exploration and travel…," op. cit.: 63-66.

53   Florence Nightingale's travel writings have been collected and published in by Anthony Satting in *Letters from Egypt, A Journey on the Nile 1849-50.* Parkway Publishing, 1998; by Michael Calabria in *Florence Nightingale In Egypt and Greece: Her Diary and "Visions."* State University of New York Press, 1996; by Gérard Vallée in the *Collected Works of Florence Nightingale, Volume 4: Florence Nightingale on Mysticism and Eastern Religions.* Wilfrid Laurier University Press, 2003; and by Lynn McDonald in the *Collected Works of Florence Nightingale, Volume 7: Florence Nightingale's European Travels.* Wilfrid Laurier University Press, 2004.

54   O'Connor. *Diary…* (October 31).

55   Ibid.

W. O'Connor's diary that clearly indicate that he had been influenced by Romanticism. When O'Connor visited Puerto Rico, he had already traveled widely and was also familiar with the travel literature of the time. He introduces descriptions that reflect his reminiscence of foreign travels. The diary highlights familiar "oriental odor of subtle beauty", "Portuguese blue" buildings, vistas that reminded him of "scenes in Greece" and the "blue of the Corinthian Gulf." His intellectual and artistic curiosity resonate throughout the diary, both in his accounts of his work and in his harmonious descriptions of his surroundings.

During the course of the twentieth century, travel writing greatly increased in popularity, making it very difficult to generalize about themes, purposes, and narrative trends. The century witnessed unprecedented technological advancements in transportation and communication (e.g., jet planes, television, computers, and satellite transmission) which facilitated rapid interaction with distant places and foreign cultures. The world entered many homes, and the "common" citizen traveled widely. Events of international and global significance such as wars, space exploration, the growth of mass tourism, and world-wide civil rights movements provided the context for many travel accounts.[56] The genre expanded and diversified into subgenres, such as war related accounts, ethnographic records, professional travel literature, tourist guidebooks, and accounts of extreme adventures to challenging and rare places.[57]

---

56   Smethurst, P. "English 2045-Travel Writings...," op. cit.

57   Hulme, Peter. "Travelling to write (1940-2000)." *The Cambridge Companion to Travel Writing*, op.cit.: 87-101; 87-99; and Bassnett, S. "Introduction," op. cit.: *xii*.

During the first half of the century, travelers generated accounts of war and its aftermath. In these, exile, escape, disillusionment, and writing from elsewhere became predominant themes. By the 1950s, mass tourism prompted travel writings that invited tourists to follow in the footsteps of the writer. The readers were expected to follow a given route, encounter predetermined places and spaces, and arrive at similar experiences and conclusions about the world as the author.[58]

At the same time, the genre was greatly enriched by ethnographers and anthropologists who visited foreign lands for the study of culture. These studious travelers searched for authenticity and for threads of connectivity between cultures. They also distinguished the unique human expressions mediated by the environment. Some seminal ethnographic works such as Bronislaw Malinowski's *Argonauts of the Western Pacific* (1922), Margaret Mead's *Coming of Age in Samoa* (1928), Gregory Bateson's *Naven* (1936), E.E. Evans Pritchard's *The Nuer* (1940), and Claude Lévi-Strauss's *Tristes Tropiques* (1955) provided new techniques for observing and documenting the foreign. This strand of travel writing contrasts with the one produced by tourists or in the context of tourism.[59]

Travel writing has been rapidly expanding as a dynamic field of study, structured by theoretical and interpretative concerns. Social, political, philosophical and personal forces mediate between the narrator and the observed. Throughout the centuries, texts captured these tensions, inviting interpretations

---

58   Maccanell, Dean. *The Tourist: A New Theory of the Leisure Class*. New York: Schocken Books, 1976: 3.

59   Rubiés, J. "Travel writing and ethnography," op. cit.: 244-259.

from historians, literary critics, social scientists, and humanists. More recently, the genre has explored issues concerning power, self perception, and cultural representation. Interest in travel accounts has expanded as the result of an intellectual climate that critically examines imperialism, colonialism, post colonialism, nationalism, and identity.[60] Currently, there is a significant and growing body of criticism and theory devoted to colonialism and its expression in travel accounts. Equally important, the intersection between travel writings and gender is increasingly becoming a topic for theoretical consideration.[61]

Imperialism, and its manifestations as a cultural and political expression of power and control, is one of the most pertinent topics analyzed in relation to travel and exploration. Travel narratives are therefore being looked at critically as a significant vehicle for promoting and even propagandizing the empires and imperial motives. Edward W. Said's *Orientalism* (1978) fueled controversy about the intention of travelers, readers, and historical interpreters of Muslim society and its people. Said argued that Muslim society was wrongly and systematically misinterpreted to perpetuate stereotypes characterizing Europeans as rational, and possessing intellectual and moral superiority. Although Said concentrated on misrepresentations of Muslim peoples, he provided a new paradigm for the critical analysis of other travel accounts which characterized African, Asian, American, and Oceanic lands peoples through European eyes.[62] This in turn has led to fresh readings of old texts, giving

60   Campbell, Mary Baine. "Travel Writing and its Theory." *The Cambridge Companion to Travel Writing*, op.cit.: 261-273.
61   Bassnett, S. "Travel Writing and Gender," op. cit.: 225-241.
62   Melman, Billie. "The Middle East/ Arabia: 'the cradle of Islam'." *The Cambridge Companion to Travel Writing*, op.cit.: 105-121; 107.

rise to a new thrust in the analysis of travel narratives.

Echoing Said, Mary Baine Campbell studied medieval European travel accounts produced by pilgrims, merchants, and explorers in light of the crusades, European expansion in the early modern era, and European domination of the world in modern times. Her book, *The Witness and the Other World: Exotic European Travel Writing 400-1600* (1988) viewed medieval travelers as agents of European imperialism, while analyzing how they "grapple with literary problems of presentation, self-representation, as well as the presentation of the other and the external world."[63]

Similarly, Mary Louise Pratt, *Imperial Eyes: Travel Writing and Transculturation (1992)*, offers a critical and daring analysis of European travelers who visited Africa and South America during the eighteenth and nineteenth centuries. According to Pratt, accounts of these travelers contributed to imperialism portraying a world that was ready for European domination. Studies by literary scholars such as Said, Campbell, and Pratt have effectively established relationships between travel accounts and imperial power.

O'Connor's diary depicts the cultural traditions and behaviors of the Puerto Rican "natives," comparing and contrasting them to his beliefs and European way of life. His characterization of the natives as indigent sick, ignorant, superstitious, unreliable at working, anemic, and lacking stamina, add to the notion of a vulnerable country, "prey to the trust monopolies of foreigners."[64] The diary contributes

---

63   Campbell, Mary. *The Witness and the Other World: Exotic European Travel Writing, 400-1600*. Ithaca: Cornell University Press, 1988: 6.

64   O'Connor. *Diary...* (November 21).

to the jaundiced and biased portrayal of the intellectual power and cultural superiority of the European traditions. Even though he recognizes the hard working and visionary pursuits of local medical professionals and health officials, there are clear references to the importance of United States medical and scientific authority and guidance. He comments that, "it was inspiring to note the genuinely good spirit in which the Spanish and American doctors mix and cooperate, especially in view of the clearly bad feeling which exists outside the profession between Porto Ricans and what they designate their U.S. 'masters'."[65] He makes continuous reference to United States influence on the island through academic and professional institutions, such as the Rockefeller Foundation and the College of Physicians and Surgeons of Columbia University, underscoring their crucial contribution.

Another recent trend in travel analysis comes from feminism and the discipline of women's studies. Scholars interested in women's literature have rescued travel writings by women, many of which were privately written as diaries and letters. Works by housewives, scientists, missionaries, settlers, and intrepid explorers have been found, covering many centuries and all continents. A critical analysis of travelogues, journals, letters, and travel literature produced by women has allowed scholars to explore gender expectations, gender-specific perceptions of the foreign, and women's conceptualization of the "self" and "others" in different cultural and social

---

65   O'Connor. *Diary...* (October 31).

contexts.[66] This has also led to comparative analyses between these writings and those produced by male counterparts. These works explore the issues of women and travel writing from different perspectives, but all of them coincide in reviving female voices and the "female gaze" of the foreign, while rediscovering the female self through history and places.[67]

In the early twenty first century there are multiple indications that travel writing as a genre will continue to intrigue. Exploration, nostalgic searches, globalization, the search for opportunities, professional dissemination, and sheer curiosity of the unknown will always motivate travelers, and strengthen the bond between travel and writing. Recent bestselling works by Paul Theroux, V. S. Naipaul, Pico Iyer, and Bill Bryson lead the readers into the new century of travel writing. The genre will always borrow from the social sciences, humanities, natural history and other scientific developments to enrich its interpretation. At the same time, first-hand accounts and encounters between the self and distant places, such as O'Connor's, will continue to provide valuable information for the understanding of the "self" and "others", inviting the readers to disentangle the multiple dimensions of the

---

66   Bassnett, S. "Introduction," op. cit.: *xiii*; and Lorcin, Patricia M.A. "Women's Travel Writing." In *World History Resources,* George Mason University: Center for History and New Media, 2003-2005. http://chmn.gmu.edu/worldhistorysources/. In her work, she argues that issues subject to comparison include: "gender, sexuality, professionalism, symbolic content, gendering the text (the feminization or masculinization of the landscape or peoples in it), the personal agendas of the authors, the context and relevance of the work to the larger picture of imperialism or colonialism, and what women did or did not achieve through their work."

67   Bassnett, S. "Travel Writing and Gender," op. cit.: 225-241.

observed.[68] There seems to be an undiminished fascination for experiencing the foreign, led by the "I" and the "eye" of a reflective writer.

---

68   Russell, Allison. *Crossing Boundaries: Postmodern Travel Literature*. New York: Palgrave Macmillan, 2000: 1-20.

5

Through a Traveler's Eyes: Landscape and Lore in Francis W. O'Connor's *Diary of a Porto Rican Trip*

Edgardo Rodríguez Juliá

iary of a Porto Rican Trip begins in a terse and precise style, without a hint of literary ambition, as if Francis W. O'Connor were establishing his scientific credentials at the outset. He resembles a Hemingway devoid of pretensions and stylistic idiosyncrasies, someone who displays only his well-ordered mind.

In a zeal for details that reminds us of the *Memoirs of Bernardo Vega*—although in the opposite direction, because the ship is sailing to rather than from Puerto Rico—O'Connor establishes the myth of the objectivity of the colonial vis-à-vis the tropics. He even echoes certain Anglo-Saxon prejudices when he tells us the opinions of a British subject concerning Puerto Rican labor in the needlework industry: "Good but Porto Ricans very unreliable at working..."[1]

---

1   O'Connor. *Diary...* (October 28).

As early as the second night on board, he begins to show his excitement about approaching Puerto Rico. On October 29, 1927, while sitting on the stern enjoying the starlit night at sea, he hears the strains of a guitar playing what he calls "Spanish songs." This marks the beginning of his increasing rapture. He sheds the more predictable attitudes of writers and travelers of that era, such as the irony of Evelyn Waugh or the feeling of superiority, however concealed, of an E. M. Forster. With that strumming guitar and that song, O'Connor begins to be seduced by the languid experience of the *tristes tropiques*. Scientific observation and detachment have already fallen prey to the virus of a magical spell.

***

Upon arrival, no sooner has the ship entered the canal of San Juan Bay and is abreast of fort San Felipe del Morro, he tells us that the leper colony, the leprosarium on Isla de Cabras, had been relocated a year earlier. This detail shows his scientific curiosity: prior to sailing for Puerto Rico he had studied public health conditions on the island. Perhaps because of this, there is a certain mastery, an air of a previous visit recalled, as he approaches the beautiful old city, the recently built Capitol Building, the School of Tropical Medicine luxuriously designed in the Moorish style, the "Spanish Revival" that was fashionable at that time.

Only when he arrives at the Condado Vanderbilt does O'Connor's description become more detailed and eloquent. The description of Santurce and the Condado Lagoon is unique, undoubtedly one of the few visits and appreciations of that sandy barren plain, covered with hicacos, which even then was considered as having tourist potential. A skilled watercolorist, O'Connor describes the panoramic view with the hues of an impressionist, taking note of the changing shades as the observer looks out into the distance. It is a description of a specific moment and place, and the reader feels an evolution, the stirring of time: "Stretching to the right, one sees the bridge connecting the San Juan Isthmus with the mainland, and further away the myriad colors of the city itself gradually fading in the distance in grays, mauve, and bluish tints."[2]

This is followed by the traveler's first hesitancy: he refers to the Puerto Rican dignitaries that he meets as Spaniards ("Spanish"), while those who were suffering from lovesickness—he points out that that most suicides are caused by unrequited love—are labeled "Porto Ricans." But he is not consistent in this, as if his gifts in describing the landscape do not extend to the people; his attitude towards the latter is ambivalent, and he seems to tread forward with leaden feet. He enhances the image of white officials with the Europeanizing "Spanish"—the same adjective used by white Puerto Rican emigrants of that time to mask their origins—and discreetly nurtures his compassion for "Porto Ricans."

Cleanliness, hygiene, and public health were the basic pillars of these medical missionaries. In his novel *La llegada,* José Luis González describes the invading Yankee army carrying toothbrushes in their hatbands. While the tropical body is sick, contemplating the tropical landscape, whose beauty marks the passing minutes, also provides a measure of respite. The quiet of the landscape from the window of his hotel room in the Vanderbilt Hotel is interrupted by the sounds of the tropical night: "The rain had ceased and peace was everywhere. The

---

2   O'Connor. *Diary...* (October 31).

frogs were chanting below in the wood and the crickets were chirruping in the bushes."[3]

He describes Puerto Ricans as people who are "naturally law-abiding." While that statement may lead us to question O'Connor's gifts as an anthropologist, we have to agree with his appraisal of our ancestral obsession for personal cleanliness and beauty, which begins with the care of our yards: "Despite the poverty, the clear spaces around the houses were kept clean and there was no evidence of refuse accumulating. There was some evidence of ambition and love of beauty at each house, as shown by the growing of bananas, a few flowers planted and blooming, and the presence of some pigeons."[4]

The description of suburban neighborhoods such as Floral Park underlines the exoticism of "Spanish Revival" architecture. At the same time, it shows the Puerto Rican's desire for individualism in architectural design that runs counter to the standardization implicit in the "American Suburban Dream."

***

This diary is full of idiosyncratic touches and sudden shifts in the traveler's attention punctuated by revealing details: after visiting Boca de Cangrejos and Piñones, O'Connor tells us how these beaches were the natural settings used in the movie *Aloma of the South Seas,* starring Gilda Grey. Our diarist indicates that this production was offensive to Puerto Ricans, which suggests that we were then, as now, reluctant to be considered exotic or underdeveloped.

Another significant detail is the assumption, throughout the diary, of a tropicalism in which laxitude and privilege do

---

3   O'Connor. *Diary...* (October 31).
4   O'Connor. *Diary...* (November 1).

not collide with the colonizer's efforts. The beauty of the landscape—be this the mountainous interior or a manicured tropical garden—adds a luxury and even a lushness to a natural environment contaminated by need, hunger, and misery. This exoticism therefore serves as the palliative remedy against the imminence of disease, a necessary intoxication, discreetly concealed, upon taking on a redemptive mission: "After a preliminary cocktail, not to be forgotten, dinner was served in the patio (or central court garden). The patio contained a profusion of crotons and poinsettias. All these could be seen by the moonlight and the reflection of candles on the table."[5] The author's enchantment is expressed in descriptions that combine the sensitivity of the painter with the curiosity of the scientist.

O'Connor is surprised and moved by our Hispanic celebration of the *Día de los Muertos*. The sense of community that transcends individual life shapes some opinions, obviously mediated by the information that he is given: "Ortiz tells me that there are not many cases of violence such as murder, etc. on the Island."[6] Accepting this statement at face value is surprising for a scientist used to verifying facts and dealing with statistics. Perhaps he had already been seduced by that spontaneous empathy with our people that was so prevalent among the travelers of yesteryear. In any case, we know that violence was always hidden, or manifested only intermittently, in our body politic.

***

---

5   O'Connor. *Diary…* (November 1).
6   O'Connor. *Diary…* (November 2).

Of course, like so many other Anglo-Saxon travelers, sociologists, or tourists, O'Connor hastens to point out examples of animal abuse everywhere. The sight of a pair of yoked oxen prompts the following comment: "We passed a bullock wagon, and one cannot help feeling that the method of harnessing those poor animals with a heavy beam and connecting their heads is cruel."[7] The Society for the Prevention of Cruelty to Animals assumes a detachment from nature that is possible only in advanced societies. Mechanical plows would replace the use of this animal as a form of labor.

Delving deeper into our hinterland, O'Connor resorts to descriptions that metamorphose into true characterizations. The architecture always seems to him to be "simple and subdued;" the people are described sympathetically and compassionately: "The people are particularly handsome in the main and dark with large gentle eyes. Many go barefoot and the women show a preference for bright orange and green dresses which contrast pleasingly with the brunette types."[8] A certain modesty and shyness, now lost, is hurriedly noted: "These people never stare at one like so many other natives."[9] As shown in the photographs of Jack Delano taken 14 years later, there is more curiosity than distrust in these *jíbaro* looks, whether aimed at the photographer or the physician. O'Connor brought with him his camera and his paintbrushes; his curiosity was sensory as well as intellectual. He was intent on capturing the evidence of an exotic culture both in images and in words.

---

7   O'Connor. *Diary...* (November 3).
8   O'Connor. *Diary...* (November 3).
9   Ibid.

On the way to Jájome to visit the Governor's residence, O'Connor keeps track of the number of curves (a total of 300!) and displays a youthful enthusiasm for details that are at once irrelevant and fascinating. His curiosity peaks and he is overwhelmed when he descends the old Cayey Road en route to Guayama. He compares this experience with ancient Greece: "As we began the descent, the vista in front reminded me of the scenes in Greece, where emerging from below Parnassus I first beheld the blue of the Corinthian Gulf."[10] The views whet his desire for a souvenir, a photographic remembrance: "The outward journey took longer owing to frequent stops so that I could take photographs."[11] If there is a secret virtue in the genre of the traveler's diary, it is this intimacy and complicity between the writer and the reader; knowledge of this intimacy evokes a sympathy tinged by tenderness.

The visit to La Fortaleza, the mansion of the colonial Governor, continues to engage the traveler's continued fascination with panoramic vistas. But the diarist is not uninformed, and he harbors some apprehension over the Spanish colonial past. La Fortaleza was also the site of dungeons, captivity, and cruelty: "one could not help reflecting on the misery of the inmates at periods in the past."[12] The black legend of Spanish imperialism would be redeemed by the angels of cleanliness, hygiene, and public health.

***

O'Connor indulges his taste for spectacular views. He returns to the interior of the island, sees the southern coast from the mountains of the Central Mountain Range, and takes

---

10   O'Connor. *Diary...* (November 3).

11   Ibid.

12   Ibid.

note of the landscape which shifts according to the colors and textures of the different crops, from pineapples grown along the coast to coffee and tobacco in the higher ground. Agriculture transforms nature into landscape, and this in turn becomes an element of production.

The description of the Hotel in the Baños de Coamo is one of the best in the diary, even when it ends with the manifestations of temper that we associate with more demanding colonial travelers such as Evelyn Waugh and V. S. Naipaul. The noise, the hustle and bustle of everyday Puerto Rican life, is the target of O'Connor's displeasure, eliciting one of the few 'neurasthenic' moments in the diary—"Consequently the would-be sleeper is forced to hear all that goes on in the hotel lounge. I heard a party in their cups discuss everything from sugar cane to love, till 1 A.M. when they retired and let me sleep."[13]

O'Connor's curiosity is endless; it focuses on topics varying from landslides, to the amatory habits of the Puerto Ricans, and the tendency towards consensual unions as the preferred way of coupling: "Many of the mountain people dispense with the religious marriage ceremony and just live together. The argument is that marriage is too expensive. Many married men have mistresses and the illegitimate birth rate is high. These children are called 'natural children.'"[14]

He remarks on local customs and language, such as the saying that "Every Saint has his day and every pig has his Saturday." Feasts are given and pork is eaten as *lechón asado*. He appreciates the karst hillocks en route to Arecibo: "One

---

13   O'Connor. *Diary...* (November 6).

14   Ibid. Part of notes made by O'Connor during talk with Lambert en route to Arecibo.

sees mountains tops jutting up from the plains." He discovers an unexpected landscape, our 'Chinese' topography, not comparable to anything else he has seen.

Like so many other Anglo-Saxon visitors, anthropologists, and sociologists, O'Connor expresses his unconditional admiration for Puerto Rican women, not because of their humility but because of their commitment to work and study. Although he does not attach the label of "matriarchal" to Puerto Rico society, he attributes to women an intellectual dedication that is lacking in men because of their promiscuity: "The Porto Rican is not a sticker at work—works in spurts. Boys good in elementary classes but in higher grades most of the exceptional students and prize winners are girls. Male inferiority may be due to [the] nature of sex life. Not much inclination of girls or boys to study music. Altogether the boys seem to lack character."[15]

***

Aibonito is described as a place where the rich take their summer vacations. Once again, the panoramic views seduce him: "A very picturesque town at an elevation of 2,000 feet and commanding splendid panoramas in all directions. This is a favorite summer resort of the wealthier people of the Island and there are a large number of pretty residences in well cared for grounds in different parts of the suburbs."[16]

The verbal picture of Ponce at sundown includes several of the elements used by Rosario Ferré in *The House on the Lagoon*. O'Connor's is also a panoramic description of the silence at dusk, when most Puerto Ricans dined in their

15   O'Connor. *Diary...* (November 8).
16   Ibid.

towns or small cities, and suggests a social characterization just as valuable as the depiction of urban life: "As it grew darker the roofs became redder, while the surrounding colors began gradually to fuse, and then suddenly and simultaneously all the lamps in the streets were lighted. The effect was remarkable, and the scene became oriental in beauty, emphasized by the stillness at our position on the mountain, from where we could hear none of the sounds of the city below."[17]

The visitor is impressed by Ponce's Casino, calling it "one of the most luxurious clubs I have been in," while he comments on the elegant parsimony of privilege in the tropics. The bouquet he is offered is an exquisite detail, an example of creole finesse appreciated with Anglo-Saxon frugality: "We drank champagne in the smoking room, and talked about an hour. Then as 12:35 we returned to our hotel and I took my bouquet to my room."[18]

His description of a stretcher ends up revealing a detail caught only by the traveler...: "two men carry on their shoulders a bamboo pole from which is suspended a hammock shaped like a cigar and completely closed. In this the patients are suspended in comfort completely covered and protected from the eyes of the curious."[19]

***

In O'Connor, an examination of the beauty of the landscape always stops short of hyperbole; there is a marked precision in his descriptions. When he describes the east coast, the view is compared to that of Samoa, although lacking the "picturesque" quality of the latter. He visits the homes of

---

17   Ibid.
18   Ibid.
19   Ibid.

the rich and appreciates their lifestyles and the architecture; almost immediately he mentions the scourge of elephantiasis, and comments on the sight of flamboyants in bloom. These contrasts, often surprising, are always tempered by small details that prompt sentimentality and a return to the pleasures of the landscape, study, or the cultivated life of the scientist or scholar: "Back at Condado Vanderbilt at 1 P.M. This morning I carried the bouquet I received last night as far as Santa Isabel till the sun was strong enough when I took a photograph of it. The rest of the day in the hotel reading and writing."[20] On the following day, after examining additional cases of elephantiasis, he takes up his paint brushes: "Spent the afternoon painting a sea view from the corner room of the northeastern aspect of the hotel, third floor."

O'Connor visits La Perla and his views of that traditional slum in the old urban core of San Juan anticipates the desolate vision of Hunter Thompson in *Rum Diary;* Thompson writes that the place is so godforsaken that it does not even appear on San Juan's city maps. More compassionately, O'Connor writes: "…last resort of degraded humanity—La Perla…The visit brought to mind Dickens's description of London squalor in the early nineteenth century."[21] This horrifying view of the old city's slum has its current counterpart in the shooting galleries for drug addicts; the homeless of yesterday have become the terrified running addicts of today, who are pursued by 'crack.' The diarist follows this horror with well-informed data: between 1926 and 1927, Puerto Rico spent $500,000 to buy shoes for its population.

---

20   O'Connor. *Diary…* (November 9).
21   O'Connor. *Diary…* (November 11).

A party on the ramparts of Fort San Cristóbal once again highlights the mixture of privilege and duty that characterizes colonial life. The scene on the ramparts of the fort is practically surrealist, and seems almost extracted from Marguerite Duras's *L'Amant*: "Here on the roof of the battlements, on cement flooring, with sky above and in bright moonlight, the Armistice Night Ball was held and I enjoyed some very pleasant dances."[22]

The rest of the chronicle will express the same disparities between human misery and the bounty of the natural landscape. When O'Connor visits the leprosarium, he describes the horrors of the disease as well as the love-making of the inmates as a result of crowding and the condition itself, especially the strange promiscuity of the women. It is a passage of rich juxtapositions and acute and intriguing observations. While describing this environment of promiscuity that evokes that of the tuberculosis sanitarium in Thomas Mann's *The Magic Mountain,* he pens the following with some sadness: "The lepers lead more or less isolated lives because they not only do not want to be seen by the outside world, but they do not like to be seen by each other. Often they do not get on well together."[23]

O'Connor visits Piñones to enjoy a picnic of *lechón asado,* travels to Aguadilla and is once again enthralled by the panoramic beauty of the place, insists on the idea of an island surrounded by ubiquitous "barracudas" on every beach, and tells us about Irish families in Puerto Rico and their lineage (the last, as part of a conversation with Dr. Antonio Fernós Isern).

---

22   Ibid.

23   O'Connor. *Diary...* (November 12).

O'Connor is the traveler who wants only a cultivated vision of the visited country; he eschews condescension, is lavish in praise, and sparing in his criticisms. At the end of his diary, in an entry dated November 21, 1927—he has been in Puerto Rico scarcely three weeks—he writes about the island: "A craze for improvement and learning. The great number of schools well attended is a good sign."

On his return trip north, he reverts to a detached, discreet, and almost constrained tone. The tour has ended; in its wake lie the enthusiasm and the curiosity of the painter, the esthete, and the photographer. As he approaches the end of his narrative, O'Connor resumes a scientific demeanor, as if he had suddenly realized that it was only proper to conceal his amazement.

CONTRIBUTORS

Ada Haiman Arena, Ph D, is Associate Professor of English in the Department of English, School of General Studies, Río Piedras Campus (RPC), University of Puerto Rico (UPR).

María Concepción Hernández, Ph D, is Professor of Classical Languages in the Graduate Program of Translation, Faculty of Humanities, RPC, UPR.

Raúl Mayo-Santana, Ph D, is Professor of Neuropsychology in the Department of Physical Medicine, Rehabilitation and Sports Medicine, School of Medicine, Medical Sciences Campus (MSC), UPR, and Director of the Institute of the History of the Health Sciences (IHICIS).

Silvia B. Rabionet, Ed D, is Associate Professor of Public Health Education in the Department of Social Sciences, Graduate School of Public Health, MSC, UPR, and Co-Director of IHICIS.

Annette B. Ramírez de Arellano, Dr PH, MCHP, MCP, works in health policy and advocacy in Washington, DC. She is the co-author of *Colonialism, Catholicism and Contraception: A History of Birth Control in Puerto Rico* and of *Regionalization of Health Care: The Puerto Rican Experience*.

José G. Rigau-Pérez, MD, MPH, is a member of the American Epidemiological Society, American Academy of Pediatrics, and Academia Puertorriqueña de la Historia. He recently retired as medical epidemiologist in the U.S. Public Health Service and holds ad-Honorem appointments in the Departments of Pediatrics and Epidemiology in the Schools of Medicine and Public Health, MSC, UPR.

Edgardo Rodríguez Juliá, is the author of novels, collections of short stories, and essays, both fiction and nonfiction. Some of his novels, originally written in Spanish, have been translated into French and English.

Ángel A. Román-Franco, MD, is Professor of Pathology in the School of Medicine, MSC, UPR. He has been Chancellor (MSC), Dean of the School of Medicine (UPR), and Chair of its Department of Pathology.

---

1   All places, locations and institutions are in Puerto Rico, unless otherwise indicated.

Anglo-Saxon(s), 13; prejudices, 239; sociologists, 244, 247; tourists, 244; travelers, 244; anthropologists, 247; visitors, 247; frugality of, 248

Anthropologist(s), 232, 242. *See also* Anglo-Saxon

Antigua, West Indies, 139

Arabia, 217, 233n

Architecture, 42, 244, 249; Spanish style or design, 17, 32, 73; design, 17n, 51, 63n, 186; Moorish style or design, 32, 38, 45, 240; American suburban, 32, 242; Spanish revival, 38n, 240, 242

Arculfus, Bishop of Gaul, 216, 217n

De locis sanctis, 217

Arecibo, 53, 54, 55, 78, 185, 246

Armadale Castle, SS, 106, 113

Arzuaga Beraza, Pedro, 171

Ascaris, 23, 37, 50, 90, 196n

Ashford, Bailey K., 6, 31n, 36n, 45n, 82n, 83, 87, 133, 153, 195, 196, 201n, 203

Asia(n), 36n, 48n, 201, 217, 233; plants, 174; South-East Asian tropics, xvi; Central Asia, 217

Asilo de Niños. See Boys Charity School

Australia, 229

Bacon, Francis, 223, 224n

Of Travel, 223

Bacteriology: discipline, 21, 27n, 98; Department of, 27, 46n

Bateson, Gregory, 232

Naven, 232

Baños de Coamo (Coamo Springs), 51, 52, 56, 246

Bayamón, 50, 78, 185, 195

Belaval, Emilio S., 159, 197n, 210n

Bethlehem, Palestine, 216

Bilharzia, 36n, 44n, 160n, 197n, 198, 199n, 211; control program, 199, 211; bilharziasis, 36n, 197, 198n. *See also* Schistosomiasis

Biblical accounts, 215

Biology: discipline of, 127, 162n, 176n; Lab, 70; Department of, 87

Boca de Cangrejos, 34, 76, 242

Boswell, James, 226

Boswell on the Grand Tour: Italy, Corsica and France (1765-1766), 226

Boys Charity School, 33, 191

Brazil, 17n, 40, 129

British: Isles, 98; society, 98n; mercantile tradition, 104; colonies, 107; Empire, 108, 229; royal family, 112n; troops, 114; army, 118n; subjects, 239; colonial usage, 76n; physicians, 174; empiricism, 225; ambassador, 226

Bryson, Bill, 236

Bundesen, Herman, 143

Burke, Alice, 49, 78, 81, 190n, 193n

Burke, Garry N., 24, 50, 60, 63, 66, 78, 80, 81, 177, 190

Burton, Richard, 229

Personal Narratives of Pilgrimage to Al-Madinah and Meccah, 229

Caguas, 42, 60, 64, 185

Cámara de Delegados, 2

Camuy, 79

Canary Islands, 104, 129

Cancer, 149, 163, 164, 180n, 202n, 208

Cape Town, South Africa, 105

Capitol Building, 17, 19, 240

Caribbean, 2, 5n, 44, 55n, 62, 84n, 157n, 160n, 200

Carrión, Arturo L., 25, 47, 48, 84

Carville, Louisiana (US Leprosarium), 173, 174, 175

Casino Club, 63

Castle, William B., 203

"Cathedral of Notre Dame" (*Iglesia de San Agustín*), 17, 19

Cayey, 43, 50, 60, 244

Chagas' disease, 161n

Chaulmoogra oil, 74, 173, 174, 175n

Chemistry: discipline, 22, 99; Department of, 21, 25n, 168

Chicago World's Fair, 142

Civil rights movement, 231

Clongowes Wood College, Ireland, 95

Coamo, 50, 51, 61, 178. *See also* Baños de Coamo

Coamo, SS, 77, 84

Coffee: industry, 3; Turkish, 35; cultivation of (plantation), 42, 50, 198, 246; workers, 170

Colonial, 4n, 11, 159n, 160n; tropics, 1, 239; condition, 3; system, 108; personnel, 156; subject, 156; situations, 158; administration, 160; powers, 159; expansion of Europe, 159, 218; governor, 245; travelers, 246; past, 245; life, 250. *See also* Colonialism

Colonialism, 160n, 233, 236n

Columbia University, New York City, xvi, 6, 9, 17n, 24n, 113n, 130, 136n, 145n, 153, 235; Department of Chemistry, 168

Columbia-Presbyterian Medical Center, New York City, 144

Columbus, Christopher, 218, 219, 220, 221

Commissioner of Health, 21, 23n, 24n, 27n, 70, 84n, 90, 143, 154n, 160, 178n, 183n, 185n, 186n, 187n, 195, 204n

Condado Lagoon, 17n, 18, 24n, 26, 40, 72, 240

Condado Vanderbilt Hotel, 17, 47, 66, 75, 78, 81, 84, 240, 249

Constantinople (Istanbul), Turkey, 216

Cook, Donald H., 22, 49, 78, 81, 82, 168, 200n

Cortés, Hernán, 221

Costa Mandry, Oscar, 27, 133n, 152n, 153n, 156n, 164n, 170n, 171n, 177n, 178n, 207n, 208n

Crete, Greece, 216

Crusade(s), 217, 234; crusaders, 200n, 216

Cueto, Marcos, 180, 181n

Leprocomium. *See* Leprosarium

185n, 187, 188, 210; parasites, 106, 181, 183; diagnosis, 46, 181, 182; and sugar cane irrigation, 57, 184, 185, 209n; elimination, 181, 185, 186, 187, 198, 210; last case in Puerto Rico, 188

Malnutrition, 23n, 166, 170, 171; and 65th Infantry Regiment experiment, 167

Malinowski, Bronislaw, 232

    Argonauts of the Western Pacific, 232

Mann, Thomas, 171n, 250

    The Magic Mountain, 171n, 250

Manson, Edith Margaret, 110, 111

Manson, Patrick, xv, 45n, 107, 108, 109, 110, 111, 112, 115, 116n, 117n, 118, 119n, 120, 121, 122, 131, 137, 140, 141, 144, 159, 189

Manson-Bahr, Philip, 109n, 112n, 113n, 114n, 115n, 116n, 120n, 140, 144n

Marasmus, 23, 36, 199

Martell, Genaro ("Jenaro"), 17, 40, 50, 53, 84

Martínez, Julio Tomás, 147, 148, 149n

Mass tourism, 231, 232

Maunabo, 64

McGavin, Lawrence, 102, 144

Mead, Margaret, 232

    Coming of Age in Samoa, 232

Medical education, 24n, 80, 93, 98, 99n, 124, 127, 128, 129

Mercury. *See* Syphilis: treatment

Microfilariae, 33, 121, 138, 139, 190, 191

people, 242; individualism, 242; movie (*Aloma*), 242; life, 246, 247;

amatory habits, 246

Puerto Rico Health Review, 133

Puerto Rico Sanatorium. *See* Tuberculosis Sanatorium: San Juan

Purchas, Samuel, 222, 223

    Hakluytus Posthumus or Purchas His Pilgrimes, 222

Quarantine, 89, 173n; Station, 17, 83; Hospital, 17n, 83n

Quebradillas, 79

Queen Isabella (the Catholic) of Spain, 219

Quevedo Báez, Manuel, 173, 196n

Race, 180n, 181n, 202n; racial, 165; racialized dimensions of research, 180;

    racist, 76n, 181, 202n

Raleigh, Walter, 221

    The Discoverie of the Large, Rich, and Bewtiful Empyre of Guiana, 221

Reed, Walter, 203n

Renaissance, 218, 221

Rhoads, Cornelius P., 202n, 203n

Rickets, 36, 199, 200

Rivera, Trinidad (Trina), 22, 168, 200n

Rockefeller Foundation, 8, 17n, 27n, 90, 122, 125, 126n, 129, 133,

    134, 135, 136n, 154, 155, 157, 162n, 179, 181, 183, 185n, 186, 187, 195,

    196, 197, 202n, 205;Anemia Commission, 202n; Division of Medical

    Education, xv, 1, 123, 129. *See also* International Health Board

132n

San Lorenzo, SS, 88

Sandys, George, 227

    A Relation of a Journey, 227

Santa Isabel, 84, 249

Santo Domingo (Dominican Republic), 13, 88, 151, 179

Santurce, 19, 27, 32, 33n, 34, 47, 191, 240

Schistosomiasis, 36, 44, 45n, 90, 161, 197, 198n, 199, 209, 211; and irrigation

    systems, 209. *See also* Bilharzia

School of Tropical Medicine (University of Puerto Rico), xvi, 1, 5, 6, 9, 17n, 20,

    21n, 22n, 23n, 24n, 25n, 27n, 34n, 36n, 38n, 40n, 46n, 49n, 80n, 83n, 84n,

    86n, 87, 90, 128, 129, 130, 132, 136, 138, 153, 168, 185n, 203, 209, 213,

    240

Scotland, 47n, 216, 226

Sea of Galilee, Palestine, 216

Seaman's Hospital, Greenwich, England, 101, 102, 107, 108

Serra, Américo, 24, 36, 50, 66, 78, 177n

Sex: among lepers, 75, 157; and filariasis, 193; among university students, 60,

    158, 159, 247

Shark: attacks, 26, 204, 206; shark skin-like, 37

Sherman, Henry C., 168

Smollett, Tobias, 226

    Travels through France and Italy, 226

"Society for the Prevention of Cruelty to Animals," 244

278

Uncinariasis. *See* Hookworm

Underdevelopment, 209

Unemployment, 150

Union-Castle Line, 103, 106

Union Club, 24, 40, 46, 132

United States, 2, 4, 6, 43, 77n, 99n, 122, 126, 127, 128, 149, 151, 154, 156,
157, 159, 165, 166, 170, 172, 176, 181, 210, 235; Congress, 2, 3n, 4, 173

Utuado, 26n, 53, 54, 178, 179, 195, 198, 206n. *See also* Yaws: Utuado
outbreak

Vasco da Gama, 221

Vega, Bernardo
Memoirs of Bernardo Vega, 239

Venezuela, 52

Victorian: tradition, 9; conservatism, 98

War Office, 114n, 115, 118, 119

Wassermann test. *See* Syphilis

Water quality, 168

Waugh, Evelyn, 240, 246

Weiss, Charles, 46, 75, 76, 78

Wellcome Bureau of Scientific Research, 134

Wenyon, Charles Morley, 114, 115, 119, 134, 143, 144

Western Hemisphere, 218

Women's studies, 235